To
Gayle,
On His love!
Marion

Marion Wadleigh

Nucle-Eye

Bittersweet **C**osmos

CROSSTREE PUBLISHING

Bayfield, Colorado

Cover photo courtesy of NASA.

Cover design by Toth Agency, Inc.
www.tothagency.com

ISBN: 978-0-9826958-0-7

CROSSTREE PUBLISHING
P. O. Box 392 · Bayfield, CO 81122

Printed and bound in the United States of America.

ACKNOWLEDGMENTS

I dedicate this book to Mom and Dad with much love. May you accept the free gift of the AVP so that your names will be written on the disc stored at Headquarters entitled Ransom's Restored.

First and foremost, I would like to thank my beloved CEO for inspiring me to write the pages of this book. As they unfolded, it became quite evident to me that He was the real author and I, merely the writing instrument. His generous revelations of CIA's mysteries still fill me with "the wonder of His all"!

A big thank you to my dear friends and acquaintances who helped me reach the finish line. Some of you patiently listened, some of you were a great encouragement, and some of you were necessary critics. I am grateful to Ginny Ostrom, Sondra Tipton, Glen and Sylvia Copple, Payden Bell, Sandra Dobiash, Kristy and Sean Davis, Della Bayless, Kim Lindsey, Charlotte Dean, Robert McNamara, and Jen Rumore.

Thank you also Mim Eisenberg (www.wordcraftservices.com), my editor, and Gene Toth, my cover designer and book formatter.

And a very special thanks to Ray and Kathy Spitz, without whom this book might never have come to fruition. For your tireless technical computer support and warm friendship, you are greatly appreciated.

Last, but certainly not least, thank you to my husband, whose support made it possible for me to daydream and write.

Nucle-Eye

A.D.	Antidote Delivered
B.C.	Bittersweet Cosmos
A.S.S.	Atom Smasher Specialist
AVP	All–Mighty Virus Protection Advanced Virus Protection
BT	Brain Trust Beloved Teacher
CAF	Central Air Force
CIA	Central Intelligence Alliance Collective I Am Creative Intelligence Alliance
CEO	Complete Elemental One Computer Existential Original Creative Existential One Creator of Everything Organic Chief Executive Officer Core Elemental One Cosmic Events Officer Cosmic Energy Officer Creator of Everything Orderly Creator of Every Orb Creates Everything Overall
E.V.	Electron Volt
CPU	Central Processing Unit
DNA	Distinctive Natal Attributes Deoxyribonucleic Acid
FBI	Forgiveness Based Immunization
ON	Occasional Night–light
R&R	Respect & Remembrance
TLC	Tree of Life Cross Tree of Life Crossroad Tender Loving Care
UF	Universal Father

TABLE OF CONTENTS   PAGE

NUCLE-US

Before the universe was born and the galaxies were formed upon the fabric of space and time, the "Nucleus" of all organic life existed. This Ultimate Matrix, comprised of a brilliant, energetic, cosmic "Brain Trust," a.k.a., Utmost Motherboard, is a nuclear, creational "think tank" called the Central Intelligence Alliance (CIA). Unlike an intelligence-gathering entity, this alliance is the original intellectual source from which all intelligence is then disseminated. The CIA, or Central, as it is also called, is operated, and headed by a multi-aspect Being known as CEO. His name has many meanings and stands for many things. He is first and foremost the Complete Elemental One and also the Computer Existential Original, the Creator of Everything Organic, and the Chief Executive Officer, just to name a few. Collectively, the CIA makes up the "Nuclei" of everything that exists. It is no coincidence that it is pronounced Nucle-Eye, because it literally knows all and sees all! All Intelligent Design is birthed from this Core Elemental One—CEO. This fundamental Ultimate Computer brings forth intelligent design through digital, quantum, and string physics. The CIA intentionally designs, expresses Itself, and describes every thing through computation. All atoms are made up of *bits* of information. Every *thing* is made up of atoms and their frequencies of energies or bandwidths. Physics is a software program understood only through calculation. Computation

1

has the power to describe all things. Mathematics is *the* universal language. The Nucle-Us *is* the original, complete primary bit—*It is!* One Almighty Bit *is*! Everything exists because of this Nucle-Us, revolves around it, or is held together by it. *It* is the origination and distribution Center of all gravitas, or as scientists have named it, gravity.

HEADQUARTERS

The home of the Alliance or Central is a massive, exquisite, mobile stellar station known as Nucle-Eye Headquarters. Formed in the shape of a small, planet-sized organ, this technological wonder possesses the most sophisticated optical shutter capabilities. When it wishes to be invisible, it simply goes into "private eye" mode by changing its electrical field, and thereby renders itself completely undetectable. Hewn out of highly-compressed, crystallized carbon, Nucle-Eye Headquarters radiates its piercing brilliance through surrounding, hard, shiny, faceted diamond walls. Impenetrably strong with unimaginable vistas; a technological wonder with no rival, this "observer" sparkled long before the Universe was conceived.

Lush gardens with crystal-clear, flowing springs and majestic forests dotted with magnificent waterfalls cover about three-fourths of Headquarters. There are thousands of acres of magnificent flower gardens and fields. Roses, orchids, tulips, azaleas, and bougainvillea of utter perfection dot the landscape in every color combination imaginable. Drinking life from the light inside the station and the misty canopy that bathes them every few hours are fields of lilacs, violets, lilies, irises, petunias, marigolds, jasmines and so many more it would take hours to list them all. Passing through the flower gardens and fields is a spectacular color and fragrance feast for the senses.

The enchanting flower perfumes are purposefully vented to waft into the City areas. Vegetable gardens, fruit gardens, and luxuriantly abundant orchards and vineyards tantalize all who come near. The vineyards are dripping with lush, large, juicy, ripe grapes in deep red-blue shades and misty-yellow greens. Some are perfect for munching, while the smaller varieties are perfect for the Headquarters' wine presses. The orchards are heavily laden with the most exquisitely perfect and luscious fruits of oranges, cherries, peaches, plums, apples, persimmons, pomegranates, bananas, coconuts, figs, dates, and nuts.

Beautiful crystal sand beaches composed of translucent crystalline that you can actually see through are kissed by an expansive, tranquil, gleaming, sapphire sea whose edges morph into the color of jade. Other sand-like beaches made up of the tiniest, milky-white pearls are opaque and emit an elegant shimmer as the foamy aqua sea gently washes over them. Brilliantly engineered, the sea in the stellar station is located in the middle of Nucle-Eye Headquarters so that everything surrounding it may have access and enjoyment. Built directly over the center of the sea, the City resembles a massive, round island in the heart of the station and lends it a pupil-like appearance. Three sets of twelve suspension bridges lead to the City from the four corners of the station. Looking like spokes on a huge wheel, they become streets as they touch the island ground. The bridges and streets are made out of transparent golden-hued surfaces. Adding gold sparkle to the color of the sea below, they give Nucle-Eye its iris-appearance finish.

The City areas are perfectly planned and carefully constructed. Imposing, sensory-activated, radiant, pearl-white walls and gates of pure gold rise to meet those who approach. Everything is made out of rare, opulently rich materials such as marble, pearls, gold, diamonds, and other precious jewels of every kind, while creating an amazingly grand, yet totally clean, minimalist feeling. The unspoiled streets feel cushiony soft, yet look like some kind of very thick, pliable glass, imbued with gold dust and diamond chips. Visually beholding these streets alone will take your breath away. Strikingly brilliant, sparkling, and awash in light, they seem to take on a life of their own.

The Capital of Headquarters, where CEO's Corporate Offices are housed, is the heart and powerhouse of the stellar station. All light emanates from it. A river of crystal-clear, hexagonal water runs through the City and flows by the Capitol building. At the foot of the river, in front of the Capitol, stands a 30-foot tall figure, encased in a clear, shatter-proof dome. A tribute to what is considered CIA's finest work, this miniature replica stands in honor of Their Masterpiece. The figure looks like some kind of twinkling, twisted tree of lights constructed out of various shapes that float and gyrate inside the display—a commemorative model of a chromosomal DNA helix. At the base of the figure a plaque reads, "The Tree of Life."

The outskirts of the station have millions of perfectly planned and constructed housing communities. Gigantic warehouses filled with endlessly imaginable things are spaced throughout the community areas. Thousands of open animal parks teeming with precious creatures of every kind dot the landscape. Frolicking and enjoying each other, their exquisitely prepared environments and satisfying provisions, the animals are having a blast. Located within one of the animal parks are CEO's stables. This is where the stallions go to retire when they are completely exhausted from playing and socializing and when they are summoned. They adore being called and getting to spend time with their Master. He always gives them love and special treats. To experience the entire length, breadth, and height of Headquarters is truly a complete sensory as well as "eye candy" trip!

BRAINSTORM

Inside the Corporate offices of Headquarters, CEO and His Brain Trust (BT) have been at work brainstorming and designing something most incredible. CEO is sitting in front of what appears to look like a gigantic, 30-foot translucent wall. He broods as the Brain Trust hovers over Him. Powerful thoughts come to life. As He speaks, the wall begins to turn into a humongous screen. Lights appear, the sound of rushing waters bursts forth, and holographic pictures with writing start to dance across the screen. Having already conjured up a "Three-Fold Plan," He reviews it once again. The "Nucle-Us" are collectively content with Their brainstorming results regarding the structure and framework of Their upcoming plans and agree, *Let Us begin!*

The legal groundwork and guidelines are established for Their plans. Contracts are initiated that will have perpetual legal consequences. With lightning-fast speed, lists of names start to be compiled. First, hundreds of names appear, then thousands. With stellar speed and sequential precision, hundreds of thousands of names flash onto the screen, until hundreds of billions of names dance by. When the last name finishes being displayed, CEO burns the data onto a tiny master disc, runs three back-up copies, and then carefully places them into the first of three CIA record vaults.

PHASE ONE—THE AIR FORCE

At the completion of the contractual documents and recorded names lists, He begins the first phase of His immense Three-Fold undertaking. Plans are afoot for creating a force of Secret Agents who will be employees of the CIA. They will be a vital part of CIA's organization and work, helping to carry out Their plans and designs, as well as providing Them with company. Prior to mass production of these beings, CEO outlines their creational purpose parameters, i.e., job descriptions. The thought-activated, translucent wall screen comes alive again when He begins to conjure up the drawing and designing of the Agent prototypes. Desired are envoys, warriors, ministers, builders, healers, etc., whose job requirements will largely be relational. They are intended to bring the CIA fellowship. So that they may relate to each other, they will be made in a likeness *similar* to the CIA, but not *"in Their image."* As envoys, they will mirror and reflect CIA's will, essence, and personality. They will be morally responsible to the CIA and under CEO's authority.

The BT's and CEO's creative thoughts continue as the screen reflects brain activity once more. Physically the Agents will not be bound or limited by time because they will be produced before the fabric of time is laid out as a dimension. They will, however, be limited by the dimension of space. That is, they will be able to live and act outside of time, but they will have to move from one place or point to another, and they will not be able to be in more than one place at a time. Because of their Secret Agent status and future covert operations' requirements, they will have physical morphing capabilities. They will be gifted with great strength, intelligence, and the capacity to make conscious choices based on free-will decisions within the scope of their job requirements. They will have a personality similar to CEO, with deep and sensitive emotions and the freedom to make moral choices for themselves by being given CEO's "endowment." They will all be made in masculine form to reflect CEO's masculine aspect. He plans to produce millions of them at once, with unique personalities. They will not be limited by the dimension of time; thus, they will have no need for reproduction and will not be given reproductive systems with their resultant sex drives.

As the CIA thinks, so it becomes. CEO very much enjoys the creational process as He personalizes His work and creates their individualities. Just like snowflakes, no two will be exactly alike. One by one their DNA helixes begin to dance across the translucent screen and manifest. All these amazing Agent beings are being built to be extremely powerful and are programmed with "Voice Activation" response capabilities. CEO and His BT invented and perfected this technological art. He intentionally programs these beings, and everything He will design thereafter, to have the ability to respond to His Voice commands. When the final DNA helix formulas are conceived, CEO once again downloads and burns all the data onto a tiny disc, runs three duplicates, and then locks all but one copy into the second Headquarters' vault.

Taking one perfect copy of the Agent DNA helixes, He goes into the Capitol's Great Ruby Hall, where the holographic life simulator machines are temporarily housed. The Great Ruby Hall is constructed out of miles of transparent, glistening, ruby panels seamlessly fitted together. The ceiling covering the panels is vaulted by two massive ruby arcs. Beneath the inlaid ruby floor is the continued shape of an inverted pyramid also made out of ruby. This three-mile long Great Hall, located in the Corporate Offices of the Capitol, radiates its light and energy and actually looks like a giant, glowing, pulsating heart within the crystal diamond station. Once the "Nucle-Us" is completely satisfied with Its work, CEO switches the simulator machines from draft mode to final production. One by one, living beings start to appear as the massive birthing production is launched.

They all have the same basic physique, but no two are quite the same. Some are slightly larger or smaller, and there are differing skin shades and hair colors. Most have only two arms, but a very few actually have four or six. Observing the ongoing production of multiple legions filling the Great Hall, CEO and His BT beam. The clatter of thousands, then hundreds of thousands, and finally millions of feet upon the translucent ruby floor fills the Hall with exuberant sounds reminiscent of multiple thunderous gigantic waterfalls. While the CIA looks on lovingly, the scene continues to unfold with the newly-created beings breaking out of their inert conditions into movement by stretching their wing-equipped arms for the very first time. Soaking up the bandwidth of the warm rosy aura inside the Great Ruby Hall, the newly-created Air Force of Secret Agents comes fully alive. The Nucle-Us is well pleased. Joy rings out at the CIA upon completion of Its amazing living Secret Air Force.

SOCIALIZATION

As millennia roll by, the CIA personally meets with all Its Agents and oversees their growth. Depending on their level of expertise and experience, they begin to find their niches and their way within the Central Air Force hierarchy. There are many ranks and chains of commands, as well as endless, exciting work opportunities. CEO's highly-organized mind is revealed as they observe His smooth-running, well-organized Air Force.

The early eons of the CIA are punctuated with many festivities. They celebrate life often. They form friendships and share joyous fellowship at sumptuous official banquets, with tables laden with unbelievable delicacies. Thousands of Agents are gifted with beautiful voices, and thousands more learn to play musical instruments. Agent choirs and orchestras take shape and assemble for the pleasure and enjoyment of all. The gleaming diamond Headquarters radiates a most beautiful aura of lights and harmonious sounds. A mutual bond of affection is growing between the Agents as they grow to know each other, and between them and their CIA. Loyalty and reverence for CEO comes naturally. He is, after all, marvelously creative, gracious, just, and lovingly kind.

He takes His beloved Agents to His stables, within one of the Animal Parks, and shares His stunning stallions. He has tens of thousands of herds of winged stallions with flowing manes in assorted colors.

Their graceful and splendid physiques are a sight to behold. When the Agents meet these noble steeds, they find themselves in breathless awe. They are physically beautiful and perfect, in endless color variations, as well as personalities, and there seems to be no end to the "wonder of it all." An exceptionally large, beautiful, milky-white stallion, with a pearlescent glow and a flowing mane and tail, immediately trots over to CEO and paws at the ground before Him. CEO caresses his forehead and neck and climbs onto his back. They both take off like the wind and race out of the Animal Park toward the sparkling sand and gleaming sapphire sea. It is a glorious sight. The Agents find steeds of their own and join in the fun. They all race and play together, chasing each other until everyone is completely sated with the joy and exuberance of the event. With pride and great joy, new bonds are formed as Agents stroke the muzzles of their already-beloved stallions. Having so much fun together, they just can't imagine life getting any better than this.

The Agents become more and more familiar with the Animal Parks and all their inhabitants. Having been created in perfection and outside of time, the animal species are preserved and do not have reproductive capabilities. They are fed with Headquarters' provisions and do not feed upon one another. They enjoy each other and their differences. The Agents marvel at the breathtaking beauty of the tigers, lions, and panthers. Millennia are spent getting acquainted and playing with all the interesting creatures. They enjoy the elephants, giraffes, gorillas, the fun-loving chimpanzees, and other assorted monkeys. They frolic with the pandas, koalas, and brown bears. The colorful parrots and birds, with their playful antics and lyrical warbling and chirpings, bring everyone non-stop entertainment. The seemingly infinite array of animals brings unending investigative possibilities for growth and fun. The CIA spends many eons allowing the Agents, the animals, and Itself to get thoroughly and intimately acquainted with each other, while having the time of their lives, before they decide to move on to Phase Two.

CEO gives two of His Agents the title of General Central Air Force Chief of Staff, with a four-star ranking because of their great leadership skills. Each of them is given a third of the Central Air Force (CAF) Agents to command. They are named "Little CEO" and "Strong Man." Little CEO is actually the tallest, and has full, straight, shoulder-length flaxen hair that frames his fine facial features, and azure-blue eyes sparkling with life. He wears a sky-blue robe trimmed in gold. His strong alabaster feet are covered with golden sandals adorned with diamonds and sapphires. Strong Man, on the other hand, though slightly shorter than Little CEO, has a broader physique and is exceptionally powerful. Curly auburn hair crowns his ruddy, freckled face, and he has deep, warm, brown eyes. His strong feet are covered with gold sandals trimmed in diamonds and rare topaz.

The third General, who is named Rotiart, is chosen by CEO to be His Personal Assistant and General of the CAF, with a five-star ranking. This fifth star is the star of special favor and grace. Handsome in every way, he becomes CEO's most trusted Assistant and beloved confidant. No other Agent has a higher rank than he has, and no other Agent has as much access to the CEO, or a more intimate relationship with Him, as Rotiart. CEO loves His Agents and they love Him. Their bond grows closer as they are shown their dwelling places at City Headquarters, the beautiful gardens and forests, the Animal Parks, the spectacular beaches, and the endless possibilities for new adventures. They joyfully anticipate CIA's new ideas and projects when they have meetings together.

IDOLATRY—FIRST CASE

Rotiart's beauty and rank, and the fact that he has unlimited access to the great CEO, cause the other Agents to be in awe of him. After all, the power of the CIA exudes from CEO's very Being. Omniscient power and limitless Imagineering capabilities are systematically birthed from Him. Just being in His presence is an awesome experience. Wherever the CEO goes, Rotiart is usually right behind. Some of the other Agents begin to hold Rotiart in higher esteem than they should, just because of his close proximity to CEO. The Agents also take far too much notice of Rotiart's physical beauty, enhanced even more by his dazzling emerald eyes, his thick, wavy, raven hair, and his full, ruby-stained lips. His flawless mocha-colored skin covers his perfect bone structure. The cardinal-colored robe, trimmed with gold braiding and sash he wears cannot conceal his strong broad shoulders. Gold sandals with diamonds and rubies accent his perfectly-formed feet.

He is also the most musically gifted Agent. He has trained to masterfully play dozens of musical instruments. In addition, he spent many millennia training his powerful, beautiful voice to sing perfectly. The CIA and Company immensely enjoy his performances. CEO affectionately calls him His beautiful song bird. After receiving a few more eons of adulation from his peers, especially from his rank and file, Rotiart begins to feel more important than he actually is. In eons past, he could receive adulation with a sense of humility. However, the tilt of his chin has reached new heights as he now pompously struts about.

PHASE TWO—THE BIG GROWTH

After 9,000 eons, the CIA, pregnant with Intelligent Design, is nearing the delivery of the second phase of Its Three-Fold Plan. The very first embryonic chip of its kind is about to be fertilized. Tinier than an atom, it is fully loaded and programmed with all the necessary attributes of the most powerful computer system ever imagined. CEO plants this hot cosmic egg at the "event horizon" of His well-chosen growth medium—the rich, fertile soil of a black, spatial womb. In loving anticipation of the unbelievably mind-blowing birth to come, the Master Architect reveals mysteries about His CIA when He lovingly pours Himself into the project and fertilizes "the Egg." In doing this, CEO becomes "the Father"! In all His designs, he sets certain patterns. Eggs or seeds are usually female receptacle components, while fertilization software processes are male. At inception, all the Intelligent Design software of the CIA is embedded into this "nuclear" seed so that germination may begin. Like a seed underground, a baby in the womb, or a bird in its shell, darkness hovers over the deep until life bursts from the womb and is born out of its darkness.

CEO shares an intriguing analogy with His Agents so they may better understand what they will witness and behold in the eons to come. He tells them:

Envision time-lapse photography of a tiny seed in the ground growing into a giant tree with branches that reach far into the sky.

The tiniest seed can become the largest tree! Due to the length of time the growth process requires, one cannot actually witness the explosion of growth. However, if you were extremely patient, you could capture the entire event on a CIA camera and play it back hundreds of years later at very high speed. With this method, the tree may be seen virtually and quietly exploding into existence. The tree will continue to grow until it dies and falls back to the event horizon and darkness from whence it came!

In a symbolically similar way, My Universe will be born and begin to grow, while conforming to prescribed laws of highly-advanced geometry and quantum physics. Where there is light, there is life. The galaxies and nebulae (universal DNA helixes) will move away from each other as they grow larger and larger each second. With precise, geometric, fractal algorithms, the programmed baby Universe will begin its structured dynamic growth. The growth method will express itself in geometrically-based calculations and million-fold reiterations performed at faster-than-lightning speeds. Galaxies will form and grow with repetitive, spiral-like fractals. The hyper-expansion growth event will lock in a specified universal temperature, as the simultaneous expansion process locks in uniformity. Electro-magnetism (gamma rays) and gravity (My gravitas) are the same strength at the moment of birth, but gravity begins to weaken as growth creates more dimensions and spreads it thinner. This allows the Universe to expand and grow and not fall back on itself. Although the stars vary in temperament, space itself will have a constant temperature.

To repeat, I create My designs from advanced mathematical disciplines. The secrets of life are hidden in the maze of extreme sizes within the Universe; the structures of the massive look very much like the microscopic. Atoms are composed of "the basic three": protons, neutrons, and electrons, which are the fundamental building blocks of everything seen and unseen. Within every atom lies the nucleus around which everything revolves. Atoms can also be described as frequencies of energies. When compounded they can also create differing bandwidths.

Upon the establishment of the "three foundational building blocks," there will really be nothing new under My magnificent kaleidoscope! Most black holes act as cosmic compost bins, while a few certain others act as cosmic wombs and are programmed with rotational energy to spit out cosmic seeds and continually reseed the Universe. Everything will continue to combine, recycle, and recombine endlessly within the incredible Universe. Cosmic, galactic, and nebular blooms will seasonally burst in and out of existence, causing the Tree of Life to flower in perpetual vibrancy, color, and renewal.

Heed My Voice—I always use a womb of darkness! Everything I create must pass through one. It is My soil and growth medium. Life, maturation, and perfection can only be achieved after successfully pushing through darkness.

The Agents ponder the wisdom they are given. Some scratch their heads, and some think they understand what He means, but most of them have yet to learn many things in order to truly grasp the significance of what He has just shared with them.

CEO continues:

My signature fingerprint may be seen in every aspect of the Creation by all who wish to find it. And My Voice will be overlaid upon the foundations of space and time. Let there be life!

And so the Universe is born and begins its dynamic growth.

17

CROSSROAD

CIA and Company enjoy watching the breathtaking, kaleidoscopic fireworks display emanating from the now-mature Universe. It is bursting with colorful cosmic blooms of every kind. When millions more eons pass and the Universal tree grows sufficiently strong and adequately large branches (galaxies) in it to hold Nucle-Us' next plan, the wall screen at Headquarters lights up again from CIA's cerebral activity. The image of the Universe appears. All eyes are focused on the wall as a thick, deep red vertical line slowly begins to creep up the middle of the screen. Once the vertical line is in place, a shorter horizontal red line creeps across and intersects it near the top. The screen reveals the geometric shape of a crimson cross superimposed over the image of the Universe. The cross appears to lend the wispy Universe a trunk. Gazing at the newly-drawn hefty stick figure, the Agents are wondering what it could possibly mean. The sounds of whisperings fill the Great Hall as many Agents flex and share their conjecturing skills. They are extremely curious about its ultimate significance, and low-key mutterings can be heard as quizzical looks abound on their faces. Rotiart ominously feels a chill up the back of his neck. He rubs it quickly to push down the hair that has just stood up. CEO tells the Agents that the crimson intersection is the "Tree of Life Crossroad" or TLC for short. Rotiart is the first to confront CEO and ask Him what this means or what the CIA is up to. "Are you planning to add something to the design of the Universe, or are you trying to reinforce it with this bloody spine?" asks Rotiart in a very bold and pointed manner. Still feeling ominously unnerved and shaking from the vision, he almost demands an explanation from CEO. But for the first time, CEO does not answer directly. After flashing Rotiart a blank stare, He looks down, throws a save on His work, and exits the screen. The CIA takes a collective breath and redirects the conversation.

After a pause, CEO once again lovingly resumes speaking and sharing metaphorical insights with His Agents. As the Father, He loves to be intimate with His creations and enjoys sharing facets and mysteries about Himself and His BT when He deems it appropriate. Looking up again, facing Rotiart and the others, He says:

The Tree of Life is now strong enough and ready to bear first fruit. When the fruit of My labor is ripe for the picking, We will all enjoy the harvest together. Ah, but I'm getting ahead of Myself. First, We're going to scope out and handpick perfectly ripe, spatial fruit. The fruits of My Universe are the orbs, but they must be the right size and shape and at the proper maturation point. After We locate the perfect, ripe fruit, We will begin setting up a round "treehouse" which must have the proper lighting and temperature and be in the strongest, upper-most, central part of the Universe, i.e., at the intersection. The geometric cross superimposed over the picture of the Universe that you just viewed reveals the crossroad of My Universe. It is the strongest area and where Our focus and work will take place. Then, We will fill it with many things We enjoy here at Headquarters, and We'll create some uniquely new things which you will get to see and enjoy with us.

The listening Agents look at Him quizzically again. But He just smiles and tenderly says, *"You'll see."*

IDENTITY THEFT—FIRST CASE

One spatiotemporal day, all the fuss over Rotiart and the compliments he receives from the other Agents infect his hard drive. The compliments are a type of new software that mutate into a destructive virus, and something goes wrong with Rotiart's Central Processing Unit. The constant bombardment of the "unbalanced" software of flattery, adulation, and praise, which he has freely allowed to enter and feed his hard drive, turns into a cancerous-type virus of pride and jealously. It is at this weak, unbalanced spot that the virus is able to get a serious foothold and corrupt his CPU. Sickness replaces healthy thoughts and attitudes, as arrogance is allowed to take up residence. The virus chips away most of Rotiart's positive programming and ultimately leads him to believe he can be CEO (the One who has created him).

He tries to convince other Agents under his command that he is as capable as CEO. After all, in his mind, he believes he is the second in command already, just one step away from being top dog. Self-delusional, with unrealistic perceptions of his own grandeur, he is quite good at imitating and copying things on a primitive level. He purposes in his mind to copy and imitate the CIA's ideas and plans whenever he can get away with it. Thus, the very first case of "identity theft" is born.

PHASE THREE—REPLICATION BEGINS

CEO has so much fun creating and making things, the eons seem to fly by. CIA and Company are up and running. The Universe has grown and matured into an immense and brilliant Tree of Life, and CEO is now able to focus His attention on the fruit of His labor. His true heart's desire, the third and final phase of His Three-Fold Plan, the purpose for growing the Universe in the first place; a need and desire for the Nucle-Us to reproduce Itself. They are excited at the thought of having offspring with whom they may share love, intimacy, and all celestial and cosmic splendors. After all, even if you have everything, it's not as much fun if you can't share with family and friends.

These new beings are already known in the mind's eye of the CIA, and their names are burned on the first set of master discs kept in CIA's Vault One. These are the as-yet unborn offspring. The Company of Agents who report to the CIA will eventually report to these Heirs. They will be given "complete free will," which will not be limited by employment parameters. They will have the ability to love or reject their Maker during a specified season, just like the Agents. But unlike millions of Agents produced at once, only two CIA prototypes will be created.

The CIA (or Collective I Am) will instruct, direct, guide, and raise up Their offspring to become loving, responsible, and dependable beings. After all, one day they will be given complete access to Head-quarters and its Company of Agents. This tremendous gift must be respected and will not be handed over casually. The transition will require maturation, as well as supervisory monitoring of the offspring's characters and intentions. The Agents will be included in the raising, protecting, and guiding of the children. Like a nanny, the Agents will be entrusted with watching and caring over the nursery. Together they will enjoy and share the growing-up process. Once the children are mature and their hearts' intentions exposed, just as those of the Agents' will be found out through process they will be given authority over the nanny and the right to judge it. That is why CEO says, *"His Heirs will at first be a little lower than the Agents. And when all is finished, the last shall be first, and the first shall be last."* Through this interaction (rubbing) process, the heart, character, intention, and devotion of both His Agents and Heirs will be exposed.

FIRST FRUIT AND THE FUN SYSTEM

CEO will first make a "place" where they can live and mature into the beings they are destined to become. Designing the habitation for Its soon-to-be-created Heirs, CEO and His BT are barely able to contain Their excitement. The Agents who know about the plans and will be assisting are happily anticipating the new adventure. CEO informs them that they will have a part in all the upcoming social events, besides nanny duties. There will be new friendships, endless things to discover and learn from each other, and many things to celebrate together in the future.

A hush falls over the gathered crowd of Agents at City Headquarters as the great translucent wall comes to life from CEO's powerfully active mind. He casts His eyes upon a particular grouping of orbs within a certain galaxy that is at the crossroad of the Universe. These spheres have grown into a cluster of perfectly ripe fruit for His design schemes. Desiring the proper lighting, He says *"Let there be illumination,"* and the Agents are dispatched into deep space to monitor the positioning event of specified colonies of stars in this particular galaxy branch. There are many, varying sizes of orb fruit, and yet He singles out one, which He decides will be just the right size for His envisioned treehouse. He sends a storm of asteroids to rain down on it, melting the iron in the soil so that amino acids are born to set the stage for life. This orb is going to be the one upon which He will lavish His favor. It will become the "Apple of His Eye"! Working with His Agents to cultivate the perfect environment, He dispatches them again and commands, *"As above, so below."*

The gardens of Headquarters will be replicated on a much smaller scale in a designated area on the orb that CEO names the Sanctuary. He employs the Agents to assist in the terra-forming process, as the topography and landscaping is envisioned for the remaining areas of the orb. Monumental gorges are excavated. Extruded rock and dirt form mountains and hillsides. Forests are planted. Seeds harvested from CIA's seed banks are transferred to designated areas on the orb. The oceans will be grand and powerful. All orb matter is pre-programmed to respond to the commands of His Voice. Agents in their various capacities are privileged to oversee, check, and assist in the final detailing. Everybody is filled with excited anticipation.

CIA names the orb "Favored" because it truly is in Their eyes! Tender Loving Care has been expended by everyone to bring about its fruition. Next, CEO commands Favored *"to twirl around its heat and light source star, while spinning, so that no area will be too hot or too cold."* That star is a gift to Favored, and He names it Fun, because of all the fun the light and heat will bring to the living beings and creatures upon it. He happily anticipates the fun His kids will have in the summer playing on the beaches and swimming in the surf created for them. In His mind's eye, He already sees surfers "shooting the curl" and "hanging ten."

To protect Favored from the spatial flak of meteorites, asteroids, and comets (universal tree debris and other falling fruit), this cluster system contains two especially large orbs within the midsection of the Fun system. The largest of these orbs and the one closest to Favored is named Jove. Jove's purpose is to catch and draw to itself spatial flak (falling debris) before it can do harm to Favored. Jove is 318 times larger than Favored and is therefore able to draw and handle humongous flying debris. It has a very small, solid core (which is 10 times the size of Favored) and a huge, gaseous outer core. This gives it a sponge-like surface for flak to bounce off of and/or be absorbed into. It hangs just beyond the asteroid (tiny fruit and debris) belt.

The second largest orb, named Cronos, is 95 times larger than Favored and is twice as far from Jove as Jove is from Favored. Cronos draws so many loose space particles and flying debris that it has attracted three distinct orbital rings around itself. The CIA planned these large orbs to be in just the right part of the Fun system, in order to protect Favored and the future Heirs.

The CIA also provides Favored with a satellite to create tides and waves for the seas and oceans. It is one-fourth the size of Favored. This large size relative to the orb is what stabilizes Favored's axis and gives it its four seasons. Without its satellite, Favored would be like a rudderless ship, and its axis would be radically different. Like a tightrope walker using a long pole to give himself more equilibrium, this perfectly-sized distant mass, in just the right spot, acts like an amazing stabilizer. Many other orbs in the Fun system also have satellites, but they are much, much smaller relative to the size of the orbs they revolve around. Therefore, their pull and influence are not nearly as significant, and none of the other orbs are privileged enough to have seasons. The satellite also acts as a kind of night light, as it reflects back Fun's light, and along with the Fun star, will become a future means of time measurement, education, and awe for the inhabitants. The satellite orb is named "Occasional Night-light" or ON for short. One side of ON is always very dark and cold, while the other is intensely light and hot. This is because ON does not spin while it twirls around Favored. Additional orbs within the Fun system have a place and purpose for the protection of the orb and its future inhabitants.

CEO commands unfathomable amounts of hydrogen atoms to combine with atoms of oxygen. The results pour onto the Apple of His Eye. Water settles into oceans, seas, rivers, lakes, and ponds as He planned. Then He commands the waters: *"This far you will go and no farther!"* From space the Agents gape in complete awe and utter fascination at how the oceans, seas, and lakes stay in place while spinning upside down, by the mere command of His Voice. As they all stare and gasp in amazement, CEO gently smiles at them and says, *"It is all held together by My gravitas!"* A long, reverential hush falls over the crowd as the understanding of the immense gravity of His love sinks in.

The Agents fill the ground with all kinds of microchip, non-hybrid seeds that will bring forth life after their own kind. The Outer Space Company gazes upon Favored as it hangs and twirls within the universal galactic tree branch, and though it is not anywhere near finished, they are proud and pleased with their collective efforts. Applause and praise go out into deep space, with reverential awe for CEO's latest masterpiece.

In due season, the seeds bring forth trees, bushes, grasses, flowers, fruits, vegetables, and all things programmed in them. When the trees reach maturation, a canopy-like environment develops, causing Favored to look even more amazing. From space it looks more beautiful than before, especially compared to all the other orbs. It is brown from the good dirt, green from the lush vegetation, and blue from the tremendous water infusion. This perfect mix creates a mystical atmosphere surrounding Favored. Nowhere else in the entire cosmos can such a beautiful, perfectly designed, inhabitable orb be found. The Universal Tree of Life was grown for the express purpose of supporting its lovely, round, treehouse. CEO looks at the luscious, perfectly-ripe, fruitful

Favored in all its magnificence and says, *"It is great!"* The entire host of Headquarters celebrates with songs, cheers, applause, and what seems like endless praises. Everyone is pleased with CIA's latest masterpiece.

The more CEO creates, the more new ideas He comes up with. His Imagineering and Intelligent Designs appear limitless. Each new idea and invention leads Him to another new possibility. Having created this magnificent orb, He sets out to fill it with all the toys and fun stuff He can imagine. He thinks that it will be endlessly entertaining and educational for His children to live and grow up inside a zoo. Just like Headquarters, animals will be a huge part of the picture. The Heirs will have constant opportunities to learn about relationships and caring for other living creatures.

FROM HEADQUARTERS WITH LOVE

From the Headquarters archives of His fascinating animal types, CEO starts a wholly-perfected cloning process for orb population: As above, so below. He also experiments with some new prototypes. These orb-specific prototypes amuse and entertain Him and everyone at Headquarters, but they are very primitive and large. The ground literally shakes under their feet as they roam the orb in aggression. Even the new experimental birds are huge and imposing. In His love, He lets them exist and have fun for centuries, and when their life batteries run down, He chooses not to re-activate them. He decides they are too giant and dangerous to be allowed to coexist with the Heirs. Their DNA is stored in CIA archives.

Cloning of animals from the Headquarters' collections continues to perfection. CEO enhances some of their features for adaptation to life on the orb. He adds reproduction capabilities that are voice activated and then clones several species of whales, dolphins, sea lions and endless species of fish to fill the seas, lakes, and streams.

When CEO clones His tiger, He smiles. All His creatures are magnificent, but the tiger is truly breathtaking. He clones the leopard, the cheetah, and the lion with the male's regal mane. He continues with the great elephant, the hippo, the rhino, the zebra, the giraffe, the gazelle, the bear, the noble horse, the donkey, the camel, the llama, the cow, the sheep, the elk, the deer, the moose, the caribou, and the reindeer. He moves forward with the wolf, the bobcat, the lynx, and thousands more. Creatures like the cow and goat will gift milks and butters that can be made into many yummy things. He continues with reptiles and creatures that creep. He also creates many living recycling machines. The orb worm is a miniature compost maker that aerates the dirt and helps everything grow better. Even the lowly ant exhibits fragments of CEO's mind-blowing organizational skills through its highly-organized social structures. Though very small, it is the ultimate orb recycler. Once again, He reveals facets of Himself and secrets of life, which He imbeds in the extreme sizes of His Universe. His Intelligent Designs and Tender Loving Care pay attention to the tiniest detail, and everything has a place and purpose.

Like a master painter working his canvas He looks at the sky and thinks it will be more beautiful if it has life in it. He clones birds of every kind. Some are just like those at Nucle-Eye Headquarters, while some variations are made to be orb specific. He makes bats so they will pollinate the trees and bees so they will pollinate the flowers and make honey. Butterflies are made to pollinate flowers and add beauty and mystique, and to show His children a literal symbol of the wonder of rebirth. The animals He creates bring Him great joy, and He is never sorry He made them. He supplies everything each species needs for them to live well. He wants to provide His Heirs with fun, fascination, and endless diversity in this mega-marvelous zoo built for them. Using voice-activated instruction, CEO now speaks to the software in the living creatures on the land, in the sea, and in the air, that *they should reproduce according to their own kind.* And when He finishes verbally programming everything, He observes that it is all exceptionally great.

FIRST ATOM

Nucle-Us now begins the third and final phase of Its Three-Fold Plan. CIA and Company travel to Favored. Upon reaching Their destination inside the area CEO has named "The Sanctuary," They assemble and wait in excited anticipation. The Company of Agents is holding its collective breath as CEO reaches down and grabs a handful of Favored's dirt. Having made the dirt, He knows all the potential that lies within this raw material. After all, everything is atomically connected to the Universal tree, because everything is in it and of it. Everything on the orb is made out of the dirt in it, and sooner or later will return to its event horizon. The dirt from the orb (fruit) came out of the tree and is also part of it. By doing this, He reveals more of His mysteries. Everything His future Heirs will learn to build will come from the dirt on the orb. Houses they will build will come from trees that first come out of the ground. Pottery will be made from clay found in the soil. All raw materials such as ore, minerals, oil, coal, tar, gas, etc., will also come from the ground. From these materials and their further combinations aided by water, they will build and produce everything their imaginations and desires cause them to think up.

He fashions the good dirt into the form He has in His mind's eye, somewhat the way a potter would fashion his design, but with superior artistry and craftsmanship. Inputting an exceptional CPU and hard drive, He adds special circuitry and software packages into the Heir. Initializing His work, He adds His "endowment" software—the thinking, willing, moral, and emotional part that makes the Being a unique individual. This gift of endowment which the Nucle-Us has also given to Their Agents is intended to be an everlasting gift. Even if the hardware crashes or wears out, the endowment will ultimately go on existing under the relational jurisdiction of the Voice. The Being is given a transfer factor of Nucle-Us' pure, consecrated transmission fluid containing millions of cells with membranes. The cell membranes act as the gatekeepers to allow helpful substances to pass through, while rejecting harmful ones. The Heir will thus receive CIA's DNA (Distinctive Natal Attributes) and genetic code, which will make him in Their likeness. DNA is a three-billion-lettered program telling every cell to act in a prescribed manner. That three-gigabyte genome sequence represents the prime coding information of the Heir's body: information-processed life numbers—in other words, physics as a software program. The Heir will have great creativity and intelligence capabilities. This child of the CIA will be given complete free will and, like the Agents, will have the right to choose how he wants to live and ultimately where his endowment will spend eternity. He differs from the Agents in that he is made *in the image* of the CIA and will be given the gift of replication.

When all is ready, CEO energizes the super batteries and gives him the kiss of suscitation to open his lungs with His breath of life. The perfect male being stands up. Physically tall and muscular, he has beautifully bronzed skin, his head has a crown of deep chestnut-brown hair, and his eyes are the color of rich, warm topaz. CEO is overcome with love for him. As he stands up for the first time and his eyes reveal the sparkle of life, choirs of Agents burst into praise songs. CEO calls the male He creates "Atom" because he is the first fundamental building block of CIA's reproduction. He once again uses His favorite phrase and says of His new man child creation, *"It is great!"* CEO says to Atom, *"I am life, and My life is in your transmission fluid."*

CEO and His Agents have already prepared the special area they are standing upon to meet every possible need Atom may have. This Sanctuary was designed, planned, and cultivated to rival any tropical paradise filled with water parks, fresh fruit and vegetable gardens, recreational parks, and animal parks. Running through the center of the Sanctuary is a beautiful river filled with refreshing, hexagonal water. Sturdy log bridges allow passage from one side to the other. In the center of the Sanctuary, at the foot of a lovely waterfall, which appears to point the way to the cherry groves, sits a monumental figure encased in a clear, shatterproof dome. The figure is a replica of a twinkling, twisted tree of lights, constructed out of various shapes that float and gyrate inside the display—a miniature, commemorative, replica model of a chromosomal helix. At the base of the figure the plaque reads: The Tree of Life.

Apple trees are dropping their fruit, and the peach trees are full of fresh, luscious peaches. There are plums and cherries everywhere. The nut trees are ripe and full of goodness, as are the bananas, dates, figs, and pomegranates. On the ground, Atom finds strawberries, blackberries, and blueberries. There is so much for Atom to explore and learn. Treats of all kinds beg to be tried and tasted, and he has only just begun. There are streams, waterfalls of all sizes, lovely grottos with hot springs to soak and bathe in, and soft grasses where Atom can refresh himself and sleep or sit down and talk with his Universal Father (UF).

He has a lot to learn, and CEO wants to teach him so he won't have to learn life experiences on his own. At some point, CEO deems Atom ready to be given charge over the Sanctuary—to tend and keep it. Atom is proud of taking over a responsibility and acting a little bit more like his Universal Father. They have wonderful times talking and walking together, and CEO enjoys sharing more of Himself with Atom each passing orb day. One day, as he wanders to the center of the Sanctuary, Atom discovers the monument at the foot of the waterfall and asks UF about it. CEO answers, *"It contains the secrets of life, and when you are mature enough you will comprehend the mysteries of life and the Universe."* With awe and wonder, Atom visits the monument often, hoping each time he does, his mind has grown mature enough to grasp the secrets of the twinkling puzzle.

UF brings the animals to Atom and lets him name them. Atom has great fun seeing all of them and playing with them. There is wonder in his eyes, as in those of a child going to his first zoo, but in reality, Atom actually lives inside a glorious zoo built for him. He enjoys all the animals very much. He spends years bonding and playing with the horses and learning to ride them. He finds several whose personalities he adores and rides them daily. They ride like the wind across the sandy beach and frolic in the sea together. Sometimes UF rides with him. The tigers and lions roll over and purr loudly in pleasure when he scratches their cheeks and necks. They often cuddle together in a pile napping in the afternoon sun with Atom using them like bedding and fluffy pillows. The elephants lower their trunks so he can climb onto their backs for a ride while directing them to the tall coconut trees laden with fruit. After they pull down the coconuts, their heavy feet easily break open the hard shells, so that Atom and the other animals can enjoy the milk and meat inside. The chimpanzees run to him with hugs and kisses; they hold his hands as they play together and forage for bananas, dates, and nuts to munch on. The birds, singing and chirping, bring music to all their ears. Some of the parakeets and cockatiels love to land on Atom's head and play in his hair. He enjoys the tingling feeling he experiences as they walk about and gently pull thin strands of his hair through their beaks. They give him kisses and do tricks to amuse him. The playful parrots, as well as the parakeets, learn to mimic some of Atom's words, which really tickles him.

After many decades, Atom realizes there is only one of him on Favored. Many of the animals have reproduced by now. They all seem to have mates, and during those times, Atom sees less of them because they are busy with each other. Eventually they bring their children around to meet all the other creatures and, especially, Atom. He is overwhelmed by the cuteness of their babies and watches eagerly as they grow up. Although he is made in the image of his UF, and looks somewhat similar to the Agents, he still feels uniquely different and alone. Atom hoped that in getting to know all the animals, he would find one that looked more like him. The monkeys come as close as he can find, but they are still quite different from him. And though they amuse him and give him much love and friendship, he still feels something is missing; this unique loneliness keeps gnawing at him. Nowhere has he found a completely suitable companion to share his life with. Having been given all the pleasures of the Sanctuary and its lovely features, he doesn't understand why he is feeling this emptiness. He has sweet fellowship with his UF, but that perplexing emptiness remains.

COMPLETION OF THE ATOM

Finally his pangs of restlessness and desire for more drive him to query UF as to why he feels this way. UF smiles. He has waited for this moment. CEO had purposefully withheld a facet of Atom at his creation, so that he was left with a sincere need. He wanted Atom to come to the realization of that need, so that when CEO fulfills it, he will truly appreciate the gift. Fully aware of Atom's frustration and glad he finally asks the question, CEO says to him, *"It is not good for you to be alone. I will make you an Assistant."*

He tells Atom that He needs to take out one of his rib bones so that He will have a DNA copy from which to properly clone his Assistant. He wants Atom's Assistant to have the same Distinctive Natal Attributes. The rib bone will be used because He is making his Assistant from his side to be his equal—neither from his head to be over or above him, nor from his feet to be beneath him, but from his side to be his equal and very near his heart to be loved by him. CEO informs Atom that although his Assistant will be of his bone and transmission fluid, she will also be wonderfully different from him and bring life to their relationship. When the day comes for the surgery, Atom is ready, excited, and aware he will feel no pain because of the anesthetized sleep CEO will put him under. Just prior to the surgery, UF kisses him on the forehead and reassures him that all will be well. *"You will experience*

35

things afresh and never again feel quite the same once you awake into your new completeness," CEO says. Atom eagerly lies down on the soft bed of grass where CEO takes one of his ribs and carefully fashions his helper.

When Atom awakes, UF places the hand of his Assistant into his. Atom stares in wonder at the handiwork. He had looked forward to having a companion who was like himself to share life with, but this, this, is so unexpected and wondrously peculiar! He looks into her azure-blue eyes, and his heart literally skips a beat as he feels strangely unable to breathe for a moment. Her sweet, full lips are the color of pomegranates, her skin is fair, and her long hair shines like gold. When he manages to catch his breath again, he names her E.V., which is short for Electron Volt, because she is the electrifying part or unit of energy that completes him. He enjoys the gift that she is. A silly grin appears on his face every time he thinks about her. He is instantly and inexplicably attracted to her, as she is to him. She is incredibly beautiful, soft, and physically different from him. Her figure and milky skin beg him to touch and gaze at her. He senses something inside him come alive, as he strangely feels more complete. He thanks UF and says, "She is of my rib and body, and I love her."

The two are very happy as they play together with their animal friends and grow to know each other within the Sanctuary. Atom happily introduces her to all the animals he has come to know and love during the decades when he was alone, and all the things he has observed and learned thus far. He is proud to be able to share his knowledge and experiences with her, and she is impressed by all he knows and his leadership qualities with the animals. There are seemingly endless new things to explore, see, and do. Their lives are exciting and fun. Atom lovingly takes E.V. by the hand and walks her to the base of the waterfall in the center of the Sanctuary, where he shows her the Tree of

Life monument. Together they share the fun of attempting to solve the mystery of the helix formula, but neither is yet the least bit capable of doing so.

At the completion of E.V., even the Agents are left in breathless wonder over her beautiful, elusive, captivating, and ethereal qualities. Headquarters is all abuzz over E.V. and how she completes her Atom. To each other they describe Atom as a magnificent cake and E.V. the impeccably decorated frosting finish.

CEO enthusiastically shouts, *"This is very great!"* His couple is made in the genuine likeness of the CIA—the two are to become "one" just as He is with the BT: complementary, harmonious and complete. They should literally mirror the aspects of their parents and continue to replicate these traits. Together they represent the first Collective I Am (CIA) prototype. Although uniquely different, they are one, and unbeknownst to them they reveal facets of the CIA. The uniting of His couple is a covenant created by CEO, and He warns that what He has joined, no one should separate.

His couple is faultlessly beautiful, strong, and supple. Clothes are not necessary because the Sanctuary is the perfect temperature for His prototypes, and they are always wading and splashing in the waterfalls and small pools. The grottos provide a variety of terraced, hot mineral baths where they are able to enjoy bathing and soaking. Hanging gardens overflow with bountiful delicacies that feed their eyes, as well as their stomachs. Magnificent flowers fill the air with exquisite perfumes, and beautiful varieties of hummingbirds complete the delightful picture as they dart in and out and hover while feeding on flower nectars.

The knowledge of sex has not been introduced into their software at this point. They have everything they could possibly want or need, and together they are having a blast exploring their marvelous surroundings, getting to know each other, and playing with their beloved animals which are tame and provide soft sleeping surfaces. They both love to snuggle in a pile with the big cats that happily provide soft bedding in trade for being stroked. Atom and E.V. are usually lulled to sleep by the sound of their sweet purring. In the heat of the day, they and the animals cool off inside the various grottos filled with cool swimming holes and playful waterfalls. The animals know instinctively which areas are perfect for them and which are exclusive to the Heirs. Some of the waters running off from the hot springs mix with the colder, deep well waters to make the most perfect tepid baths. CEO and His Agents have even fashioned a natural stone staircase that leads to a funnel-type slide. When Atom and E.V. finish climbing to the top, they are able to slide through two frigid cascading waterfalls and land in a warm swimming hole.

Dolphins and orcas offer exhilarating rides through the calm sea for the mere price of affection. They are like large slippery, fun, affectionate dogs. The very few insects that exist are all beneficial and do not bite or sting. Tame bees provide the sweetest and most delectable honey variations for their pleasure. Atom and E.V. savor berries and nuts and drink the cool, clean, refreshing hexagonal water from the waterfalls. The air is filled with soft breezes and the Fun star warms the orb with radiant heat. The ground releases the heat at night to warm them and the animals, and the night brings peaceful rest. The waterfalls and wading pools bring refreshment. There are delectable treats everywhere, and life is a pure joy. These are truly wonderful times for both CEO and His Heirs. CEO is very pleased with His work, and just like any proud new dad, He is completely taken by His precious children. Atom and E.V. are wide-eyed with wonder, pleasure, and love. Atom is thrilled with his new companion and has never been happier. CEO visits with them daily, and He shows them and teaches them new things every day. He walks with them in the lush gardens. He rides the horses with them on the sandy beach. This is their season of bonding, learning, and growing.

One day CEO gives Atom and E.V. authority over all of Favored. It is time for them to assume control and responsibility. It is also a necessary testing of stewardship, and a way for CEO to observe how responsible and loving Atom and E.V. will be with all the treasures entrusted to them. Occasionally they ask their UF to explain and solve the mystery of the Tree of Life, but CEO just smiles and tenderly says, *"When the time is right, you will comprehend. After you are mature and responsible enough to be given all the cookies in the cookie jar, you will have the ability to understand."*

THE COOKIE JAR

CEO shows Atom and E.V. all He has made for them and tells them that they may freely partake of everything He has made (which includes millions of things), except one. This item, He tells them, is to be reserved for Him. He wants only this tiny percent of everything they have, so He will know that they love and respect Him by honoring the single boundary He sets before them.

On one side of the Sanctuary, amidst the cherry trees, CEO has His Agents cut the top of a medium-sized tree to a height of about five feet. They smooth the surface so it becomes a table that is slightly hard to reach. CEO now places a clear glass jar with its contents on top. The contents look like chocolate chip cookies. The jar has a lid on it with a seal. CEO tells them that this jar and the 30 cookies inside are off limits. They are not to open the jar or eat any of the cookies until He personally gives them permission, and if they do ingest the cookies, it will harm their still-new battery packs and transmission fluid, causing their hard drives to malfunction and eventually crash. The cookies are ingestible software discs loaded with chips that impart knowledge, but CEO tells them they must wait until their systems have matured and built up sufficient anti-viral and antibody protection to safely take in the software.

In addition, if they disobey Him, they will lose and forfeit their stewardship and authority over Favored. He promises to share the cookies with them when the time is appropriate and their anti-viral and antibody protection is mature and ready. He also wants to see if they will follow His instructions, so He can entrust them with more goodies in the future. For now they need to just trust and believe Him and not eat from the cookie jar or they will experience physical death and lose title to Favored. In other words, everything is a "do" and there is only one "don't."

INSUBORDINATION—FIRST CASE

The Company of Agents celebrates and praises their CIA. Outer space is literally abuzz with excitement over the completion of marvelous Phase Three. Seemingly endless parties and banquets are held to commemorate the accomplishment. At the conclusion of one of the many incredible banquets, Rotiart and his crew are finishing up with hot cups of mocha nectar and assorted desserts. After eating a blushing peach, Rotiart slices an apricot into sections. Holding the apricot sections under a fountain of melted chocolate, he savors each bite. He and others also reach for the luscious strawberries and hold them under the fountain. As he relishes his last cup of the mocha nectar, he motions to his close circle of friends. Tossing a chocolate truffle in his mouth, he quickly grabs a handful more to stuff into his pockets for later. Some of his buddies follow suit, and then they take their leave to follow Rotiart. As he and his crew look back in the direction of the banquet, smiles can be seen everywhere. Joy is pervasive, and everyone is having a wonderful time.

While an orchestra is playing praise music in the background, they hang out together and rehash their recent, shared activities: how they enjoyed their last horseback rides and races by the sea, their latest accomplishments, and what they plan on picking out and getting the next time they are at the warehouse. Waiting for the right moment to plant some doubt and discord, Rotiart pops another truffle into his mouth before he speaks. His mood is clearly not in line with everyone else's. Instead of being happy for the CIA and joining in the fun, he has developed a peculiar myopia. He cannot envision the future joy they will all share together. All he focuses on is that he is no longer the center of attention and that CEO does not meet with him as frequently as He used to. He is seething with jealousy!

Hoping to raise some envy and strife, he runs some negative thoughts by his underlings who are gathered around him. "Haven't you noticed that CEO doesn't think we are enough for Him? Even though we will love Him forever, He always wants more. When I was in His Corporate Office at Headquarters, I tried to warn Him that 'these Heirs' will disappoint. They will complicate matters for all of us and become His and our great regret. With their total free will gift, they will bring Him pain. But He dismissed my counsel! I conclude that we will never mean to Him what these two prototypes already do. And as they replicate, they will become as numerous as the stars, driving a wedge between all of us and CEO, ultimately displacing our standing in Him. We, the employees, will be supplanted by these new-comers. And why does this have to be so?" He continues, "And have you also not noticed that He did not build us with the capacity to repro-duce? Yet He freely gave that gift to them!" Some of the Lieutenant Colonels, trying to comprehend the new concerns possessing Rotiart, ask him if he has spoken with CEO about his feelings and if CEO has explained any of this to him. Rotiart simply hisses back with, "He is always preoccupied with *them* these days!" Rotiart's cohorts, their curi-osity piqued because of his accusations, are now overcome with inquisi-tiveness because of all this strange new input.

Still popping truffles, they all head for the Corporate Offices, and sneak into CEO's equipment room. Activating the powerful telescope, they fill in the query box that asks for a subject. The telescope instantly turns in the direction of Favored and brings the two prototypes into sharp focus on the huge screen in front of them. The complicitous Agents are now keenly studying their features. After all, their supervisor has just informed them that these two Heirs are going to be a menacing threat to their futures. Staring at the characteristics of the male and female, they especially take notice of their intriguing physiques. Shaped like a pair of beautifully limbed, lithesome trees, their heads are splendidly crowned with hair. Completing their magnificence are strong jaw lines that support high cheekbones, and eyes sparkling with life. They also observe how lovingly and inseparably the two interact. They look at each other, nodding in agreement that the male and female together look strangely familiar. After a pause, concerned looks creep across their faces as their fascination turns into trembling when they notice the uncanny resemblance to the great Collective I Am!

Rotiart's hard drive continues to be eaten up by the vicious virus he has welcomed. The parts that are programmed and obedient to CEO's voice commands are now rapidly disintegrating. He adjusts the telescope's focus to gaze upon Favored from outer space and begins coveting the lovely, luscious, ripe fruit twirling in perfection before his eyes. He knows the orb is filled with majestic mountains, trees, oceans, lakes, awesome waterfalls, flower fields exuding hypnotizing fragrances, and every good thing the CIA has thought to create. Beholding the beauty of it all and reflecting on the work he and the other Agents have done to help bring it into its fullness, his countenance begins to change.

Then he once again fixes his gaze upon the perfect prototypes, and something inside him snaps as he begins to shake with a seething, violent jealousy. Steam comes out of his ears and nostrils, and his normally stunning, brilliant emerald eyes turn blood red. "We were the object of His affections, and now He lavishes it on them! How dare He replace us! Why are we not enough for Him! We must rescue Him from the folly of His actions." Jealous of the Heirs and angry at the very One who has given him life, Rotiart begins scheming to find a way to rid himself of the objects of his animosity and gain control of Favored. The first "green-eyed monster" has been born and with it, the iniquity of coveting.

DAY OF R&R

CEO is so thrilled and pleased with His new masterpiece in Atom and E.V., His future hopes for them, and everything He has provided that He at first doesn't notice that Rotiart is not behind Him as he usually is. He decrees that a special day of rest be set up so that all will remember the wonderful work of His hands. CEO tells his children that one day of Favored's week should be set aside out of respect and remembrance for His gifts of goodness to them. They should honor Him and praise Him for all He has done on their behalf. The Day of Respect and Remembrance is to be called the Day of R&R, and observed by refreshing themselves in rest, feasting, and praising their UF.

MORE IDOLATRY

Rotiart thinks Favored is magnificent (as does everyone), and he doesn't want CEO's children to have authority over it. In his newly-acquired arrogance, he decides he will take control of it for himself and eventually supplant CEO. About one-third of the Agents, who are under Rotiart's command and in his constant proximity, willingly catch his insidious virus; they also freely choose to voice activate to Rotiart's commands. By doing this, they shift their allegiance and worship from the Great CEO to their Commanding General. Thus, the very first mutiny has been hatched within the scheming heart of CEO's favorite Secret Agent. Having partners in crime, Rotiart becomes ever bolder, and his followers more idolatrous.

FRACTURIZATION VS. FRACTALIZATION

Rotiart overheard CEO tell Atom and E.V. of the "don't" boundary. He thinks to himself, *If I can get them to transgress the boundary, I can destroy CEO's perfect genetic code. My act of mutiny will mutate their DNA before they are able to replicate. Once transgressed, Atom and E.V's battery packs will stop maturing and eventually malfunction and die. After that, all their reproductions will be fractured by inevitable death. I will save CEO from Himself. This will break the terms of the contract and I will inherit control of Favored. And He will be better off without them.* Rotiart has figured out the theory of "divide and conquer." While CEO creates through fractals and makes everything whole, Rotiart takes what is whole and fractures.

Rotiart is a highly intelligent Agent with a very large and efficient CPU, a massive hard drive system, and huge memory banks. He devised the best way to approach the couple. He knows that if he can get E.V. to eat the cookies first, Atom will simply follow. Atom is the physically stronger of the two and is programmed to provide, protect, and tend to his work. Rotiart has also observed how infatuated Atom is with E.V. Being a male Agent whose brothers/buddies are also all male, he is not able to relate or empathize with the male-female bond of love that Atom and E.V. share. Unable and unwilling to understand that bond, he relishes the thought of putting a wedge between them. She is programmed to love and keep relationship with Atom and their future offspring. She is also the birthing womb CEO has designed to bring forth new replications.

Rotiart hates the relationship CEO is building with His two Heirs, and knows they will ultimately inherit Nucle-Eye Headquarters. He cultivates a special hatred for E.V. Although Rotiart is a strikingly handsome Agent, E.V. possesses a uniquely different kind of beauty. This leaves Rotiart completely frustrated and baffled as to how to compete for attention. Hers is a feminine beauty. She is alluring, and extremely captivating, with an ethereal, hovering quality that mimics the BT. She has become the talk of Nucle-Eye and all Its Agents. Rotiart is no longer being fussed over, and his warped hard drive simply cannot process that. She is truly fetching and will bring forth many Heirs. Rotiart despises her even more than he hates Atom because she has been given the role of keeping and completing the relationships that he now desperately seeks to destroy. She seems to threaten and touch his nervous system on a deeper level. Loving relationships are the very essence and reason behind all of CIA's plans, designs, and creations. Unity between the created couple is of paramount interest and import to the CIA, because after all, this will mirror and replicate Their perfect image, allowing a glimpse into the mysteries of the multi-aspect Nucle-Us. When a complementary blend of two becomes one, the dynamic, universal law of mathematics is curiously enhanced. One plus one no longer has to equal just two. One plus one can now equal three or more.

Rotiart knows that if he gets to her, he will have successfully defeated both, and Atom and all his future children will become mutants. The CIA's desire for healthy reproductions will be terminated. As the idea sets off the light bulb in his head, Rotiart breaks into a sly smile. Talking to himself out loud he says, "Ah-haaa, so this is how you kill two birds with one stone!"

THE SPLITTING OF THE ATOM

Rotiart waits until Atom and E.V. have reached the adolescent stage of their lives. They are beginning to think they know it all and are becoming somewhat rebellious. As they grow, more hormones are being released into their systems, but they are maturing physically more quickly than they are mentally. CEO knows they need a few more orb years before they can handle the "chocolate chip cookie" software He has reserved for them.

One late orb afternoon, Atom and E.V. are resting under the shade of a cherry tree. They had started their morning quite early, frolicking with a pair of playful orcas in the ocean. The fun-loving Shamu and Sheena offered rides, and they blissfully raced each other through the gentle waves until the spirited competition finally came to an end. Atom and E.V. patted the heads of their pals goodbye and kissed their wet noses as they headed for the trees laden with coconuts, bananas, and dates. Samantha, the elephant, was so happy to see them coming that she shook the coconut trees and stomped on the fruit to make it ready for them and her fellow animals to enjoy. Everyone loves Samantha because she graciously provides hard-to-reach morsels to all those below. Together they drank the coconut's milk and ate its delicious white meat. Then they picked bananas and sun-ripened dates for all to share, while continuing to employ Samantha to knock down any unreachable treats they desired. After several more hours, they all headed for the berry patches, still snacking on their booty and picking figs along the way. E.V.'s favorite chimp, named Muffin, hitched a ride on the back of her tiger pal, King. They all strolled together until they reached their fruity destination. Luscious, huge, juicy, ripe strawberries, blueberries, and raspberries were everywhere. Still ravenous from their long walk and their earlier swimming and racing with the orcas, they greedily grabbed mouthfuls of the juicy sweet fruit and stuffed themselves. When everyone had enough berries, they moseyed over to the cherry trees. There they picked some more fruit and ate. Now tired, completely stuffed, and in the cool of the shade, they plop down together in a pile and cuddle ready to indulge in a brief, but welcome nap. As usual, King and some of the lions provide soft bedding and backrests for the weary travelers.

After an hour of blissfully dozing, E.V. awakens to the sound of someone saying, "Pssst! Over here." E.V. looks up and asks, "Is it you, beloved UF?" Rotiart's terse, "No!" reveals the anger he cannot hide. Still respectful of authority, E.V. answers sweetly, "I'm sorry, I just assumed you were CEO because He comes to visit us daily, and it is usually in the late afternoon." Dressed in a teacher's uniform, he almost chokes on his spit when he snaps back with, "He visits you daily?!" Apparently forgetting the more than 9,000 exclusive eons CEO had spent with him and his Agents, he is completely overtaken by his envy, and he has to take several deep breaths to clear his throat and regain his composure. But he quickly manages to accomplish that and looks especially dapper as he feigns continued confidence in approaching her. E. V. joyously responds, "Yes, and we sometimes take the horses and ride together along the sea." She then says, "I can see you are a teacher?" However, Rotiart not ever having been this close to the naked female before finds himself tripping and stuttering as he is taken aback for a moment by her breathtaking beauty. "Yes," he mutters, "I teach rote—er, um—I mean, I am Teacher Rote." She smiles at him sweetly, unaware of any danger, and almost manages to disarm him. But his hatred has long passed the tipping point, and no one,—not CEO, not her captivating beauty nor charming essence, and not even the other CAF Generals and Agents—can soften his heart or change his mind.

Atom, who is supposed to be the protector, is still busy napping. Hearing voices, King barely manages to open one eye. Then upon hearing E.V.'s sweet calm voice, closes it and places his paw across his face until he gently rolls from his side unto his back and blissfully stretches all four of his huge paws into the air. Sliding off his back, Muffin has to readjust herself by climbing onto his stomach and then quickly resumes her slumber. In deep sleep, Atom never moves a muscle.

Rotiart tells E.V. he was sent by CEO to teach her new things. He has now uttered one of the very first lies spoken in the Universe! He points to the cookie jar on the nearby tree table. "These cookies," he says, "are delicious to eat, and they will open your eyes and mind to new feelings and make you wiser than CEO Himself. You will know all and see all, and you will come to a fast understanding of the mysteries of the Tree of Life."

E.V. replies, "But, Teacher Rote, we were told not to touch the cookies or eat them outside of UF's presence or direction, lest our batteries fail and hard drives crash."

Again Rotiart tells E.V. that the cookies are delicious beyond comprehension and that her hard drive will surely *not* crash, but rather be enlarged and enlightened and made as intelligent as that of her Universal Father's. "You will be all grown up," he tells her. "CEO is just trying to keep you from having fun by keeping you under His control. CEO is being unreasonable in giving you this boundary. Besides, the cookies ultimately belong to you anyway. What harm can it do if you eat them a little sooner?"

E.V. remembers that the cookies are to be administered to them ultimately anyway. She and Atom have been feeling rather grown up this past year, as well as frustrated and impatient for having to keep waiting to experience this forbidden treat. Unable to solve the Tree of Life puzzle, they have been bugging CEO for the answer, but He just keeps telling them they are not yet ready.

Sensing that her resolve is about to melt away, Rotiart breaks the seal, pulls out a cookie and pretends to nibble off a corner as he says, "See, it has not harmed me. And, boy, is it delicious! That is why I am wise enough to be your teacher. And the chips are made of a substance called 'chocolate,' which you don't know how to make yet. It is the nectar of the inhabitants of Headquarters and is more delicious than anything you have ever tasted before." With Atom still asleep, E.V. is at last enticed by the conniving Rotiart. Figuring CEO would never have to know, she lets her curiosity get the best of her, she takes hold of the cookie waved in front of her face, and she takes a bite.

She does find it to be unbelievably yummy. Instantly, her mind opens to new thoughts and feelings she has never imagined. The software chips begin downloading into her brain. The new input and brain stimulation are now too difficult to resist. When Atom awakes to E.V.'s voice, she hands him a sample, and he eats. They look at each other and their eyes grow wider! *Wow!* they think, *these cookies are amazing!* And they both instantly begin to know *so* much more. A sly, arrogant smirk crosses Rotiart's face as he watches the couple, now completely engrossed in a cookie feeding frenzy. Having achieved his maniacal goal, he slinks away unnoticed into the underbrush.

They continue eating until all the cookies in the jar are consumed, because once tasted they are impossible to resist, and they are thereby uploading more and more information that CEO doesn't want their young minds to have at this stage of their development. The transmission fluid cell membranes (gatekeepers) cannot protectively screen this sudden flood of new software because their anti-viral protection is not yet completely matured. Suddenly, their eyes are opened to their own sexuality, and they blush as they look at each other in their nakedness. They also hear the new and strange sound of an alarm going off.

CRASHING HARD DRIVES
AND CONTRACTUAL FORFEITURE

The warped Agents that are following Rotiart's voice commands had put an alarm on the "don't" tree to signal when the Heirs of CIA are defeated and Favored shifts under their authority. Rotiart and his followers will have a celebration of their own now that he has successfully snatched control of Favored. The three realms of Nucle-Eye, the Universe, and Favored have been breached. Unbeknownst to the foolish participants, their actions have activated a great sifting! The purging process has begun. Loyalties and motives within the hearts of Agents and Heirs will find their true alignment after being born through trials and testings.

CEO, aware of what has taken place, is steaming mad. He goes to the Sanctuary to see if Atom and E.V. will be responsible and admit what they have done and say they are sorry. Knowing full well they have eaten the cookies, He wants to hear what they have to say. He looks for them, but they are hiding. They are busy wiping the warm chocolate off their mouths. He asks them why they are hiding from Him and if they have eaten the "don't." Atom finally replies, "Did not," to which CEO says, *"I know you have."* Once again Atom says, "Did not." Finally Atom sort of fesses up by saying "This Assistant you gave me, she made me eat the cookies." Red-faced, E.V. says, "This Teacher you sent tricked me into eating 'the don't.'"

CEO is concerned and deeply hurt because He knows that His children have ingested more information than their CPU's can handle at this stage of their development. Their young bodies and brains will not be able to safely and properly process all this new software. And they have disobeyed His instructions. Had they waited until He allowed them, life would have been much easier for them. Had they matured longer, their battery packs would have become stronger, and the "don't" would not have been able to attack their life-giving batteries and cause them to corrode, and their transmission fluid would have stayed pure. But what hurt CEO the most is the fact that Atom and E.V. did not listen to Him and then added insult to injury by lying rather than taking responsibility for what they have done. And even worse, they never said they were sorry for disobeying Him.

Before It could replicate, the perfect likeness of the CIA has been torn apart by the hatred of His favorite Agent and the disobedient choice of His children. This very first divorce in the Universe causes the Universal fabric to be rent apart, ripping the spiritual realm from the physical. The relationship between the male and female is now warped out of reflecting the perfect essence of the CIA. CEO has to let His Heirs and Agents suffer the consequences of their actions and choices, all the while hoping they will mature, repent, and realize their mistakes. When Rotiart chose to pit himself and his followers against the Heirs, the great purging process commenced. Once again, darkness will be used as a growth medium to bring the souls of His Agents and Heirs into character distinction and completion.

Queer, uneasy pulsars emanate from the heart of Headquarters. Resembling acid rain, the bitter electro-magnetic radiation oozes down and permeates into the Universe like a heavy, clammy blanket. The eerie melancholy leaves its unsettling imprint on the Tree of Life as it slowly starts to sway from a trembling, rolling rumble. Crying quasars cause hyper-novas to implode, nebulae to exhale, and many outer galaxies to break off as they are sucked back into black holes due to the great gnashing. It is the sound of CEO and His BT shedding acrimonious tears, weeping for the very first time, while the remaining loyal Agents grieve along. It is also the first time in the Universe that the Atom has been split. The jolt to CEO's heart is akin to an atomic bomb going off! When the cloud from the nuclear blast finally materializes, it creates a veil of separation between the spiritual and physical dimensions.

DIVORCE—FIRST CASE

Now spiritually divorced and trapped in the physical realm, with all its limitations, Atom and E. V. have to learn things the hard way. Being disobedient and unrepentant got them kicked out of the Sanctuary and made it difficult for CEO to help them. Now they have to make their own way and learn. With a heavy heart CEO commands two Field Marshals to guard the Tree of life memorial while it is being prepared to be brought back to Headquarters. Having downloaded all the chips in the cookies, the Heirs have a much more extensive knowledge base to work from and could possibly grasp the secrets of eternal life. If they were to decode the dimension of time, they could propagate millions of defective mutants who would never die.

CEO knows that some will come back to Him and realize their errors, but some others might forever be lost. He does not want to lose any. They have been given free will and the ability to accept or reject His love. He can do anything except make their choices for them. The very next thing CEO tells them is, *"Have kids of your own. Maybe then you will come to understand what I have gone through with you."*

They are not mature enough to properly handle the knowledge they have ingested from the cookies, so premature sex is on the way. Cut off from their spiritual aspects, they find that dynamic relationship changes are occurring. Their missing spiritual parts create a void within their hearts that they feel but don't know how to fill properly. Before the Transgression/Mutation, Atom and E.V. were complete individuals. Together they were also complementary and more fulfilled. But now, with their spiritual facet missing, they have a real need or a type of emptiness, like what Atom felt when he was still alone in the Sanctuary, and they seek ways to fill that void. Without CEO's help or restorative powers, they will turn to material things that will neither satisfy nor ever fill the actual void.

The first noticeable shift is that Atom finds all his worth in what he does or accomplishes, and E.V. now finds all her worth in relationships, especially that with Atom. Because the male and female now have differing needs and ideas on how to fulfill them, a huge gap has developed in their relationship. CEO tells E.V. that she will give birth in pain and that they will spend the first several years teaching their children to walk and talk, but by the time they are teens they will want them to shut up and sit down.

CEO's great love and wisdom foretold to Him what might happen with respect to children and free will. He is not really taken by surprise, but He is disappointed, deeply hurt, and concerned for the welfare of his children. He had hoped they would have waited until they were more mature and better able to handle the responsibilities that go with having their own, especially how to develop character in them. CEO was going to teach them all these things in due season, but now they have to do it the hard way, by trial and error. It grieves Him to have to send them out on their own and that their relationship has been broken. Too immature to admit their disobedience and feeling ashamed, they no longer want to spend time with their UF or listen to anything He has to say. They are busy exploring each other in new ways, running wild, and having sex.

He made them to be relational with Him, but now that relationship is broken. The willful disobedience of His children grieves his heart. His favorite Agent and the legions under his command have turned against the CIA. With so many eons of insider information at his disposable and his willingness to do the Heirs harm, the father of mutiny has started the first war in the Universe.

YOU'RE FIRED!

CEO summons the full complement of His Secret Agents to the Great Ruby Hall at Headquarters. Not even Rotiart is able to escape the absolute force of His will. In His grief, CEO's hair turns the color of white wool. His normally warm, welcoming brown eyes have turned into piercing flames. And His usual joyfulness is replaced with a serious resolve that has a chilling and sobering effect on the countenances of His Agents. The mood at Headquarters is decidedly altered. By now, everyone at CIA is aware of what has transpired. The next highest ranking Generals, Little CEO and Strong Man, are still in a state of emotional shock, as are most of their underlings. They are appalled at what Rotiart has done to CEO and His Heirs, yet sad for him at the same time. They were brothers. They have loved him, trusted, and relied on him, as did CEO, and they can't imagine why he has done this despicable thing. They experience emotions they have never known before. Firstly, they are deeply saddened, and secondly, they feel tremendous anger. As the Great Hall fills with summoned Agents, there are the sounds of whispering and gasping, and the sights of many tear-filled eyes. Among the legions that followed Rotiart, some are wringing their hands and biting their lips. For the first time, there is fear in the air.

Still unbelievably pained from the betrayal, CEO is sitting quietly in His official ceremonial chair, getting ready to call the meeting to order. A sea of Agents splits in front of Rotiart as he enters the Great Hall and begins strutting toward CEO. A hush falls over the crowd, as everyone in the Hall is scarcely breathing, until he finally arrives before the One who has summoned him. His loving heart still hoping for a sign of remorse from His favorite Agent, He begins to speak, *"Why Rotiart? Why? I endowed you with great beauty, gifted you with tremendous talents and status. You have been given command over the entire CAF. You were given the keys to the City and access to its complete splendor. You have a beautiful mansion and the finest stallions. We have been friends, and you have been given untold numbers of brothers. There is almost nothing I have withheld from you, or would not have given you, had you but asked."*

Rotiart, visibly shaken by the penetrating power and authority of His Voice, now trembles before the great CEO. For a few moments, warm and tender memories pass through his mind, along with some flickering embers of love for CEO and his brothers. But in his heart, he chooses to douse them all. After an unbelievably long pause, Rotiart defiantly stiffens his shaking body and glares into CEO's eyes as he menacingly says, "Just like You, I simply wanted more!" Millions of gasps echo through the Hall. Rotiart arrogantly continues. "I warned You that these Heirs would disappoint you, but you would not heed my wise counsel. They have transgressed Your law, and correct me if I'm wrong, but there is now a little legal matter here that You will need to address. They have chosen to heed my voice and follow it, rather than Yours! Isn't that rich! Therefore, according to Your own contractual laws of free will they have chosen, and are now subject to *my* authority, as well as *everything* you have entrusted to them, like pretty little Favored, just to mention one! The Supreme Court of Headquarters must now satisfy *my* claim, according to Your Own Voice." Smelling victory, he thrusts his chin upward, and a sly smirk begins to grow on his face like an ugly fungus as his blissfully ignorant glare continues.

If CEO chose, it would take just one of His penetrating laser looks to burn a hole right through the fool and vaporize him in an instant. Although provoked to anger, He is sure of Himself and His ultimate Master Plan. Fully aware that manure stinks, He also knows that it is an essential element for growing beautiful things. And being outside of time, He is long suffering and patient.

Digesting all this unbelievable audacity, CEO sits quietly and pensively for what seems like an eternity to all who are present. At last He begins to speak. *"I see that you have studied My law. What a brilliant trial lawyer you have become, the first of your ilk as a matter of fact. I would be proud of you but for the fact that you are a corrupt one, the start of what I'm sure will be many, thanks to your help! Oh, Rotiart, how incredibly sick and disappointing you have become!"* As CEO's mood grows ever somber, His authoritative Voice booms throughout the Great Ruby Hall, and everyone freezes in their stance, including the maniacally moronic Rotiart. CEO exhales deeply. *"You were perfect in your ways until you chose to commit mutiny. You willingly welcomed injustice and greed. You are now full of evil, and because you have done this vile thing and show no remorse, you're permanently fired! So close to the very top, so close to the Head of All! How far your fall will be!"* The usual lovely rosy aura that bathes and soothes everyone present in the Great Hall has now turned a harsh, crimson red. *"You are exiled from Headquarters. Any Agents who have chosen to follow you are also fired and exiled. If you ever set foot on Headquarters' soil again without being summoned, you will immediately be arrested."* CEO continues, His Voice now escalating to a roar, *"Your name is now forever changed to Traitor (Rotiart spelled backwards) for your backward, backstabbing ways, and for having betrayed your creational purpose."* Fear overtakes Traitor's very being, as he reels backward from the truth lashing, but instead of repenting, he wastes no time turning on his heels and fleeing from the great CEO.

Unable to withstand the burning condemnation of His truth any longer, Traitor and his cohorts flee out of the Great Hall as fast as they possibly can. Regrouping outside with his legions of loyal subordinates, he catches his breath and regains his composure. Away from the presence of CEO, his strength returns and the battle begins. Millions draw their weapons to overtake the remaining loyal Agents. But the legions of Little CEO and Strong Man have already mobilized and outnumber them two to one. In the ensuing melee, multitudes of Traitor's warriors are overtaken, captured, and arrested. Many, however, manage to slink away. Traitor and his Castaways, who manage to escape arrest, gleefully swoop down onto Favored like a bunch of marauding pirates. Touching ground, they laugh hysterically, rub their hands together, and salivate over the freshly acquired plunder. Once again CEO, BT, and the remaining Company weep.

DEATH—FIRST CASE

CEO strikes down a pair of sheep known as Buddy and Bitsy to show Atom and E.V. the severity of their transgression. He intends for them to understand the gravity of their disobedience: death upon themselves and all they have been given dominion over. He shows them how to make clothing to keep warm, as there is no perfect temperature outside the Sanctuary. The relational breakup caused by their rebellion cut them off from access to His life force. Like fallen branches separated from the tree trunk, the life force (transmission fluid) can no longer flow down to them. The Transgression/Mutation changed contractual authority over both the Heirs and the orb.

Having wrenched authority away from the Heirs, Traitor now begins to plot their destruction. Traitor has not become more powerful; he just acquired authority over the Heirs and the orb when they listened to him instead of CEO. The orblings must learn how to legislate their realm of authority, while understanding that there is a difference between legislating and wielding power. In other words, they have to learn whose authority they want to live under. The Wholeliness of the CIA cannot look upon or commune with the fractured, transgressed orblings. That is why CEO commands the killing of the first spotless, perfect animals. He temporarily accepts their "transgression-free" transmission fluid as a substitute payment for their iniquities.

The only way the Heirs can break through the nuclear veil of separation and reach the spiritual realm is by shedding the transgression-free transmission fluid, just like a power cord temporarily plugged in will facilitate a type of electrical connection. When CEO focuses on the perfect transmission fluid, there is a temporary reconnection, and the Heirs can commune with Him without His noticing their fractured state.

MUTANT REPLICATION—FIRST CASE

Atom and E.V.'s sexual relations cause them to bear a son they name Get. Then they have another son they name Breath. CEO watches hopefully from his screen at Headquarters and maintains communication as best He can with rebellious children who are now raising their own. He communicates with them through His Voice. He can no longer visit face to face because He cannot look upon their unwholeliness. The couple also has several daughters. As Universal Father to Get and Breath, He watches them and how they behave. CEO chuckles to Himself about Breath. He knows the name is perfect, as the child actually is a Breath of fresh air in the midst of all the darkness. Breath enjoys UF's Voice and spends time with Him. He listens to the Voice and pleases CEO. His older brother Get, on the other hand, chooses not to listen to the Voice and is downright rude at times. Breath has enjoyed the warm relationship with his UF, which he has spent the time cultivating. And over time Get becomes jealous of his brother. The Voice tells Get that he loves them both equally but that Breath's behavior pleases him more and that if he doesn't act so rude or disrespectful, he could have the same intimacy.

BLAME STORMING VS. BRAINSTORMING

By now Favored is permeated with the viral sickness of Traitor and his Castaways. They are taking up residence and affecting the bandwidths of the orb in very negative ways. Traitor also tells all his Castaways that they need to find any way they can to keep the children of the CIA from trusting Him or having any relationship with Him. The last thing they want is for the Heirs to regain intimacy with their UF and find a way back to their inheritance. Traitor knows the children were given complete free will, and he is going to make it his job, and that of his cohorts, to keep them from making the right choices. He will deceive them, lie to them, trick them, and cause them to lose their way. *If I am to be forever fired, I will drag His Heirs with me into exile.*

Then he says to his underlings, "Since CEO turned my name backwards, we will take all the good things He made in order to benefit the life of His Heirs and entice them to abuse and pervert these things. This should cause them to get sick and grope in the darkness like blind rats. They were given sexuality for enjoyment and making children. I will entice them into perversion and make it emotionally painful. I despise E.V.'s beauty and femininity, and I will enlarge the wedge I created between her and Atom. I will whisper in Atom's ear every chance I get, to make him blame her' for his hard life and troubles. They won't know what hit them, and there will be derision and strife.

We will trouble and afflict them so they won't have time to think about their UF. I am capable of mutating the primitive insect life. I will unleash fleas, ticks, flies, spiders, and the like to afflict the animals and the Heirs. I will mutate many insects and simple life forms and cause them to bite and sting with venomous, itching, or burning substances. Hopefully, they won't think of listening to the Voice or turning back to Him, and with any luck they will hate Him and blame Him for what we will actually be causing. We will suffer them to look at the orb and wonder why there is so much pain and misery. How delicious! Because of the gift of free will, even the great CEO won't be able to make His children come back to Him unless they choose to." Traitor knows full well the character of CEO and that He will not take back the gifts He has given, even if misappropriated by those He loves.

MURDER ONE

With each passing orb day Get becomes increasingly jealous of Breath, who seeks and heeds the Voice of his UF and, according to Get, is a sickening "goody-two-shoes." Get refuses to behave better or honor and heed UF's Voice. His anger and jealousy begin to resemble that of Traitor's. One day, while Breath has his back turned, Get grabs a rock from the ground and smashes it into Breath's head. The DNA within his transmission fluid cries out from the ground, and CEO knows his life has been spent. And once again CEO, BT, and remaining Company weep.

The Voice confronts Get and hopes for some flicker of remorse. When he asks Get where his brother Breath is, Get angrily replies, "How am I supposed to know where he is every minute?" Again CEO finds no contrition, just more lies and cover-ups.

E.V. is now completely distraught. Atom is furious at Get for murdering Breath. Tensions between Atom and E.V. mount. Neither of them can stand to be around Get at this time because of all the pain he has inflicted upon their family. When he shamefully runs off with his favorite sister to start a new life in a distant place, his mother E.V. grieves again. She can barely stand the pain. She lost Breath, Get, and one of her daughters within a very short time, and her life feels like it has been turned upside down. They must now work and travel distances in order to forage for food and sustain their needs. Gone are the days of the Sanctuary, where hanging gardens of fresh produce were all around them and abounded in various stages of ripeness.

The animals now suffer the same fate. Samantha, her mate, and young elephants travel great distances in search of more feeding grounds. As they wander away and roam the orb, they never find their way back to Atom and E.V. Tiger and his family have also left and head deep into the forests. When last seen, Muffin was still riding on his back, with her family following on foot. Atom and E.V. miss their animal friends but are now so busy there is little time to grieve, let alone reminisce. All the animals are extremely preoccupied with finding enough food for their expanding families. The fun, lazy days of playing and hanging out together have vanished and now seem like only a distant dream.

In his heart, Atom blames the difficulties of his life on E.V. After all, she offered him the "don't" and talked him into eating the cookies. He conveniently forgets the fact that CEO charged him with protecting her and the Sanctuary. Having lost three of her children in such a short period of time, E.V. cannot handle Atom's condemnation. She needs his love more than ever but cannot find it. The warmth he once felt for her has chilled in the hardness of their lives. There is nowhere else he can go, unless he wants to be completely alone. Ashamed, he is no longer able to face his UF.

Atom and E.V. work together, sleep together, and for a while, enjoy having sex, as it is the only tenderness they still share. Atom hasn't forgiven E.V., but he must ignore his resentment in order to get close to her. He becomes angry with himself for needing her. She needs his love in order to sustain the pain of childbirth, but she ends up facing it in loneliness, pain, and sorrow. She presses him for affection, but he withdraws. Desperate for the relationship, she yells at him when he is gone for long periods of time. Unwilling, or unable, to understand her pain and needs, he further distances himself emotionally from her. E.V. yells at Atom, "Why can't you see that it was Rotiart who tricked me?" E.V. thinks the only way to get Atom's attention is to yell at him. They have many shouting matches and rarely speak to each other civilly.

Atom, unable to properly confront E.V. and his own participation in the transgression, perfects his art of avoidance and retreat. But he is sweet when he needs her sexually in order to satisfy his emotional need. On the surface, E.V. appears to be the angrier one, especially to their children. Atom rarely loses his temper, he just walks away, leaving the children thinking their mother has lost it. Feigning innocence, he absolves himself of any blame. In their pain, the two now withhold affection from one another, and many days are spent yelling and blame storming. The children are gleaning the modeled parental behavior. The previously joyous couple is now far from happy, as the bitter harvest of their rebellious action keeps cropping up. Traitor and his buddies, observing the mayhem they helped create, snicker as they high-five each other. Once again CEO, BT, and remaining Company weep because their family has been rendered dysfunctional by the mutational transgression.

POLYGAMY—FIRST CASE

By the fourth generation of murderous Get, one of his great grandsons takes more than one Assistant for himself, and thus the very first practice of polygamy begins. CEO is not amused. Traitor's deception and hatred, however, score one more victory against his beautiful nemesis.

Favored is now filled with a great many successions of Atom and E.V.'s children, many of whom have sex the moment they reach puberty, with resulting pregnancies. They do not want to learn wisdom or abstinence. They just do what feels good or what comes naturally. Their perversions cause blockages in their circuitry and further hindrances to hearing the Voice. Without proper guidance and wisdom, they do things that cause great harm to their family structures. Traitor manages to warp many offspring, rubbing out most vestiges of any that even remotely mirror the CIA.

Working feverishly to entice the males to lust after females who are not their Assistants, Traitor easily convinces the selfish males that their female Assistants can just be used, rather than loved and cared for, and that they are inferior to them because they were not built with the same strength. CEO created the Assistants differently in order to complete (the word "complete" referring more to a type of complementary full-ness) the males, rather than copy them. Most orb males were built with far greater physical strength than their female counterparts. The Secret Agents, including Traitor and his Castaways, were built with phenomenally superior physical powers. Traitor's hatred for E.V. and her femininity continues to erupt as he whispers in the ears of the males. He always highlights their weaker traits and convinces those males who possess selfish egos to think the females are inferior instead of the wonderful addition they were intended to be. His loathing continues to manifest itself in the way he convinces the males to abuse and discount their Assistants throughout the generational successions.

Traitor also plants ideas in the heads of the males to cause many to begin to lust after each other. After all, the Agents are all male and have neither sex drives nor replication capabilities, so why not trick the Heirs, who have sexual drives, into false proclivities? "Instead of healthy friendships and bonds, I will usurp the Voice and whisper in their ears to cause them to lust after each other." Traitor gloats, "This ought to really mess up CEO's design!" In this way, Traitor is hoping to further disintegrate the image of the CIA by causing the males to reject their Assistants and prevent reproductions.

CEO longs to help His children, but they want nothing to do with Him. They become increasingly vile with each passing generation, as the sickness is passed down to the fifth and sixth successions. CEO is now truly sorry He has made them. Yet in spite of their wickedness, He still loves them and hurts for them. The children He had hoped to hold *in* His heart, now have a disturbing hold *on* His heart.

THE VOIDS OF FRACTURIZATION

Multitudes of incomplete and defective offspring have been born. Cut off from their spiritual aspect, they naturally feel an inexplicable emptiness and disconnect. Discovering that no amount of physical gratification will fill that void, they turn to false gods. They worship Fun, their light star. It brings warmth and light, and nothing on Favored can live without it. Realizing the significance and importance it plays in their lives, they worship Fun instead of the One who created it. In their depravity, they sacrificially offer up orblings to it by killing them, hoping to appease the Fun god. Because Fun is just a star, nothing is accomplished but murder, the continued wounding of CEO's heart, the pricking of His ire, and just another victory for Traitor. Others worship animal gods. Instead of admiring the wonderful qualities of these creatures, they deify some of them. The orb itself is also turned into a type of god. Many worship the mother orb. The One who actually created everything, however, is being totally ignored, denied existence, or rejected.

A PLACE OF HOPE

Atom lived 930 years before his battery pack finally failed and he expired. E. V., whose heart had lost its strength, had died several centuries earlier. Atom and E.V. had had another son they named Place, as well as many daughters and more sons.

The sons of Place stay somewhat close to their UF and love Him. Some seem to follow His counsel and maintain a relationship with their wise UF. The other children of Atom and E.V. distance themselves from the loving CEO. Multiple successions are born to populate Favored. Some of the offspring of Place want continued fellowship with their wise UF because they love Him and want to learn. CEO wants nothing more than to guide and help his children live well. Many of the other children think they know it all and don't want anyone telling them what to do or how they should live. They do not think they need any counsel and completely shut UF out of their lives and refuse to hear or heed His Voice. This grieves CEO greatly, for He knows He could save them untold misery. But, sadly, He cannot help all those who need help, only those who want it.

Place has many children and lives a total of 912 years before his battery pack finally fails. With each successive generation, the passing on of faulty genes through failing battery packs creates shorter and shorter life spans. In addition, Traitor's deceptions cause many to abuse their bodies and further hasten their degradation. He and his Castaways roam about on Favored to trick and deceive as many of the generations of Atom and E.V. they can to keep them from realizing who they really are—the sons and daughters of the CIA. Steering them away from UF, Traitor is aware they could forever lose their inheritance. Traitor knows he will live indefinitely because his battery pack and those of his Castaways were built outside of time. However, he also knows that the battery packs of the generations born of Atom and E.V. were built within a dimension of time and were not able to come to full maturity because of his deception. They will all expire after a period of time. Atom's offspring came out of E.V.'s womb, so the children were born with the same inferior hard drives and transmission fluid disconnect, which over time become more and more vulnerable to viral attacks. Traitor knows this will give CEO's Heirs less time to change their minds and find their way back to their inheritance.

CEO rarely leaves Central. He visits Favored on an "as needed" or "petitioned" basis and mostly uses His voice-activation feature wherever it is received. Orblings are hurting each other, murdering each other, and doing other sick things that the CIA never intended. Traitor and his Castaways continually whisper in the ears of the lost, "If there really is a CEO, how could He allow so much pain and suffering? Any CEO who could allow this mess, can't be a good CEO and is certainly not worthy of worship or praise!" The Heirs welcome and allow depraved and negative vibes, and CEO's Wholeliness cannot stand to be in an unwholly presence. In His love, He doesn't want to risk having His wrath and anger leak out before He has accomplished His purpose.

THE DAYS OF COMFORT

The generations of Place show signs of promise, although many of them have also become Voice shunners. There is a son born to them by the name of Comfort. The Voice had inspired his parents to name him such. Comfort sees all the destruction around him, and he cries out to his UF for help. He and his family, although also inheriting defective DNA, make a free will decision to listen for UF's Voice and instructions. They recognize His Voice, His love, and wisdom and they wait to hear from Him before they do anything. They cry out for His direction, help, and favor. This positively touches the heart of CEO.

BUILDING THE REFUGE

For the love of Comfort and his family (the only true remnant of His love), who are still relatively pure and perversion free, CEO decides to take drastic measures. Unfortunately, most of the remaining masses willingly follow sickness and seek to do nothing but that constantly. Traitor and his Castaways lure multitudes of Heirs to warp and misapply their creational functions.

The Castaways possess great knowledge and insights into the secrets of the universe. They are forbidden to crossbreed with the race of orblings. But they are always looking for new ways to defy and anger their former Boss, since he had fired them. They miss the life they once enjoyed with their band of Secret Agent brothers; those times had been so wonderful. But they do not choose to rededicate themselves to the CIA or change their ways. Instead, like a shaken nest of hornets, they continue to come against CEO's beloved Heirs with a dreadful vengeance. They figure out how to activate fertilization capabilities among themselves and entice orbling females to have sex with them so they can inseminate their wombs. By infiltrating the orbling race this way, Traitor and his Castaways intend to further mutate their DNA, hoping CEO won't be able to separate the Castaways from His Heirs. Having been fired and exiled, they are going to either destroy or take as many Heirs with them as they can.

The impregnated female orblings give birth to hybrid offspring. Not only are they exceptionally large, they are unbelievably strong, with unorbly intelligence. This mixing of the transmission fluids between Agents and Heirs is strictly forbidden by the CIA and really infuriates CEO. These hybrid beings are a menacing threat to the future of CIA's transmission fluid line. Most of the remaining Heirs choose to listen to Traitor and his Castaways because, in their sickness, they think it more fun, and eventually the virus turns their CPUs and hard drives into reprobate minds.

Because Comfort chooses to listen to the Voice, he lives well and stays relatively healthy. He instructs his children to also follow the Voice, and they do. Because of their wisdom, they avoid the degradation going on all around them. The Voice instructs Comfort to build a place of refuge that will survive an unbelievable storm surge. He informs Comfort that He has to take drastic measures to protect His remnant. He wants Comfort to build an extremely large, water craft. Comfort totally trusts His UF and, with the help of his three sons, starts building according to the Voice's instructions. This task is a huge undertaking, but Comfort knows that the Voice will be right by his side to help guide him. UF, the Master inventor and builder, gives Comfort measurements and tells him what trees to use and how to shape them, etc. All Comfort needs is patience and perseverance to finish the job. As the building of the Refuge progresses, UF reveals more of His plans to this family.

UF shares with Comfort that He needs to cleanse Favored of the sick beings, especially the hybrids. Replication of their genes has to be stopped at all cost. They have become so vile that they have reached the point of no return, and the only way to protect the remaining few healthy and innocent is to employ a radical containment plan. UF tells Comfort to talk with as many as he can who come to view the early building process, and if any choose to heed his plea, they will be welcome and allowed to come aboard. He shares with them His intentions to save His species of animals. Together they grieve for a spell, realizing the seriousness of the situation, and then continue the work that needs to be done. Many preparations must be readied, and many, many orb years will be required to accomplish this mammoth undertaking in order for CEO's remnant, and especially thousands of animals, to come through the surge successfully.

Faithfully obeying the Voice, Comfort builds the foundations of the craft with gofer wood. All outside surfaces must be coated in pitch to make it waterproof. Pitch must also be used on all the inside seams. At this point, some orblings actually help the family build, simply because they are fascinated and want to be a part of this behemoth project and learn. They help haul wood, provide extra hands for the high and heavy lifting of wood panels, make pitch, and help coat the vessel outside and inside where needed. With a large, community effort the difficult groundwork is being laid. Three young orbling females, who heed and seek after the Voice, also show up to work and help Comfort's family. They happily assist any way they can. Distributing water, bread, meat, bananas, apples, and figs, they nourish the workers so they can keep going. They also run errands and pass instructional messages between the builders as needed. They join the family whenever they spend time in petition before the Voice, and because of this, they understand the critical need for the Refuge project.

After about 15 years, no other helpers and workers seek the Voice and none catch the vision; thus, they begin to tire and fall away. The massive outer shell is almost finished, but most think this project is insanely out of reach. By now, the majority of those who came to work think Comfort is nuts, and they are not shy about telling him and everybody else. One by one, they leave the worksite in frustration and badmouth the family. The three young females loyally continue working. Having completely endeared themselves by now, they almost seem like family. The sons of Comfort have each grown to love one of them and formally take them as Assistants. With the hope, strength, and renewal that are born out of companionship and someone by your side, the sons now move forward with a new freshness and vigor for their work. The family, now happier and more complete, press on together to fulfill their UF-given mission.

Now that most of the strong outer shell of the vessel is in place, they concentrate on building the first floor. Large tree trunks are used to support the second and third floors. The center is left open to the top floor, like a huge windowless atrium, in order to accommodate the tall giraffes and elephants that will need to be housed. The bulk of water will be stored in several massive containers built right into the craft on the first floor. Wooden tanks are built for stocking different species of edible fish that will be kept on board. More water storage facilities will be located on the other two floors when they are completed. This will provide segregated watering stations for the differing needs of the animals and the family on board. The very first semi-portable potty is ingeniously designed and built on the second floor. It has a lid on it, and the lower compartment is filled with thousands of worms. A sealable door opens and the liquid waste runs down the outside of the Refuge's hull.

About 80 years later, the upper floor is finished. Furniture is built and put in place. A large, crude table is built with bench seating where the family will share meals around a small cook stove. The Voice instructs them how to build a wood-burning stove/oven out of stone, clay, and mud against the wall of the craft and how to vent it safely. When they finish building the wood stove, they are thrilled with how wonderful it is. On its flat stone surface they are able to boil water, fry eggs, and reheat meats and cakes they have baked inside the oven. They are also able to make numerous rice dishes filled with chicken, lamb, and assorted vegetables. Many years before the last of the Refuge is finished, the Assistants experiment baking breads, small cakes, and potatoes, while figuring out how to roast chickens, turkeys, lamb, and fish more perfectly. The gals enjoy using it so much, they become great cooks and create tasty meals that help renew their strength and keep them all going. Through the fun and joy they experience while sharing mealtimes, they discover what other needs they have in order to function more efficiently. Small, crude, wooden tables are built for food preparation surfaces. Wooden racks with shelves are built to hold freshly baked breads, cakes, and pies.

UF instructs Comfort to build a variety of plant beds, gather seeds, and dry fruits and vegetables. He also guides them on how to properly hang and dry the meats of deer, elk, sheep, cattle, and chickens for long-term storage. After the Transgression/Mutation, many things had changed. Orblings killed each other and the animals. They learned that the flesh of animals was good to eat and it became common practice. Since CEO was going to destroy all flesh on the orb, He wanted Comfort's family to store up supplies of dried meats for the long duration. These proteins will sustain them and the other animals until vegetation and all food sources return. The family will keep and use the many pelts for blankets and bedding. Hay is gathered and bundled. Wood is chopped and stored for the stove. The lower two floors are covered with straw, and large amounts of both straw and hay are now put into storage.

More orblings come by to view the construction process and query Comfort and his family as to why they are building a floating vessel so far from the sea. Truthfully they reply, "A huge storm surge is coming to wash away the contamination and bring viral containment. Everything you are looking at will be under water." The passers-by laugh hysterically and ridicule the family. No storms or rains have ever impacted orb life thus far, so they are unable to wrap their minds around the possibility of such an event. The orb holds a misty canopy under its clouds that moistens everything daily. The thought of a deluge of water is foreign to their thinking, and because they shut their minds to the Voice, they cannot think "outside the box." Comfort and his sons and daughters-in-law plead with visitors and other groups who have congregated around the craft to become a part of the process so they too may be saved. However, the mobs just hang around to taunt and provoke them, as they laugh and jeer and yell obscenities. In their utter perversion, they shamelessly engage in lewd activities in front of the Refuge while accusing Comfort's family of being pious, uptight, and homophobic. It becomes increasingly clear that no other orblings will heed the Voice.

Comfort's parents had been inspired by the Voice to call their son that name. CEO foreknew that this orbling and his offspring, in their wisdom and obedience, would please Him by heeding His Voice. Through them He will be able to fulfill His plans, and this does bring Him much comfort.

LAUNCHING THE REFUGE

After approximately 100 orb years, the Refuge is now complete, as well as all the accompanying necessary preparations. CEO allows this extra 100 years so that two of each of his precious animal creations will be preserved for future repopulation and also to give the Heirs more time to repent. The massive three-story-high Refuge is truly a breathtaking accomplishment, especially for a family of only eight.

Prior to completion day, the healthiest and strongest male and female of each animal species are called out from amongst them by CEO. Many coming from great distances, they begin to wander toward the Refuge in pairs. Thousands of summoned animals serenely congregate around the craft. This highly unusual and remarkable gathering begins to crowd out and displace those camped nearby. They pick up their gear and move to higher ground, especially upon seeing the coming of the elephants, giraffe, rhino, and big cats. Normally taunting Comfort's family with lewd behavior and obscenities, they're actually gaping speechlessly for the first time. Marveling in awe at the strange occurrences unfolding before their eyes, more and more nearby orblings show up to observe these unusual happenings. Word spreads, and nearby communities rush to the site and form large crowds of onlookers. Most of the animals that would normally cause orblings to run and scatter now draw a huge gathering. The fierce beasts are unnaturally docile and focused, and the stunned public is hypnotized as they watch the unbelievable event taking place. By nightfall, tens of thousands of animals have quietly surrounded the Refuge. Before the darkness envelopes the crowds, many opt to put more distance between themselves and the animals, while some head back to the safety of nearby community areas until morning.

The first light of daybreak reveals calm, seemingly well-organized processions of animal pairs meandering onto the ramp and entering into the Refuge. They instinctively know where they need to be once inside and find their places. Some crowds come back again to watch and are completely awestruck at how the animals are streaming into the craft with such peaceful, purposeful surety. In spite of the unprecedented flurry of activity, a serene atmosphere surrounds the vessel as the animals find their places, do some munching, drink a little water, and then bed down quietly to slumber in needed rest. It takes eight hours for the streams of animals to finish flowing into the craft.

Shelves on board are packed and brimming with all manner of fresh foods, as well as nuts, dried fruits, dried vegetables, dried meats, and all provisions necessary to sustain the animals and Heirs for the duration. Hundreds of live fowl are kept on the second floor in very large and ingeniously built coops. They will provide eggs, dinners, feathers, and future reproductions. Sacks filled with dried seeds of all kinds are stacked and ready for use. The water storage systems have all been topped off. Plant beds are brimming with crops of every kind, and hundreds of others are in the germination phases. Shelves are filled with carpets and blankets of wool, as well as pelts and skins. Goose feathers have been collected and stored in bags made out of skins. The beds of the Heirs are covered in sheep pelts and fur blankets. Crudely- sewn pillows are stuffed with goose feathers. They have stored up enough materials for bedding and clothing for the next ten years. CEO has helped them think of everything.

When all of CEO's summoned animals are safely inside the Refuge, it is three in the afternoon. The stunned crowds move closer to the vessel once the last of the animals disappears inside. CEO speaks so loudly both Comfort and his sons unmistakably hear the Voice say, "*You and your sons must come inside for the last time, employ the elephants to pull in the massive ramp, close the door, lay the heavy bar across, and drive the long wooden pegs in place for security.*" Orblings outside don't know what to make of it all. Comfort and his family are inside with thousands of wild animals. When they see the door shut, they walk around to see if there are any openings they can climb into to continue to spy. But with the long ramp inside, the door is much too high to reach, and they all discover that there are no other possible entry areas. They camp outside for a while and try to listen for any sounds that might be going on inside, but they hear nothing.

Having followed all the Voice's directions, Comfort and his sons make a speedy check on the animals to be sure all their provisions are accessible. Then they quickly wash up and head to their favorite family gathering spot on the third floor, by the wood-burning cook stove.

As they climb the stairs, the mingled, tantalizing aromas of freshly roasted meat, baked breads, and assorted pies waft toward them. The Assistants had been preparing food, cooking, and baking since the early morning hours. They had prepared enough to get them through several days without having to bake again. Now they are busy setting the table with pottery bowls filled with vegetables. A loaf of crusty, warm bread is on the table, and many more can be seen lining the racks stored alongside the kitchen. Cooling on one of the wooden racks and releasing their delicious aromas are two apple pies, three peach pies, and three mixed berry pies. Tiny wooden bowls filled with herb-infused olive oil sit ready. One of the warm, freshly-baked apple pies, accompanied by a bowl filled with fresh assorted berries, sits in the middle of the table for dessert. Numerous lit candles give the kitchen area and dining table a beautiful, inviting glow. On the table, upon a large, flat, grooved wooden board sits a twenty-pound, perfectly roasted, succulent turkey waiting to be carved. Wine made five years earlier and stored in large skins is served. Comfort lifts his hand-carved wooden goblet of wine, toasts his family and gives thanks to the Great UF for the bounty they are about to enjoy. Everyone gives thanks to UF and nods in agreement.

Comfort and his eldest son Fame carve and slice up the savory golden-brown turkey. Drumsticks, wings, and thighs are passed around, along with big slices of the breast meat. They rip the bread apart and dip the broken pieces in the aromatic oil. They also use it to scoop up the vegetables and wipe up the pan drippings. Hot ginger root tea is served with the luscious apple pie and other fresh fruit. Completely satisfied with the wonderful meal they have just enjoyed together, they push away from the table and begin the clean-up. They finish as dusk settles across the land outside. Then they blow out all the candles except the ones that guide them to the welcome sight of their soft, fur-lined beds. When the last candle is blown out and they are snug between their pelts of soft fur, the darkness outside descends upon the craft.

Thoroughly exhausted from all the final preparations, the family begins to slumber. There was so much to take care of in addition to making sure all the animals had everything they needed. And although quite secure in CEO's care, there is trepidation about what lies ahead. The animals, weary from their travels, watered and fed, are also resting quietly or sleeping. When the darkness of this fateful night finishes swallowing the Refuge, so does the spirit of tranquility, and everyone inside falls into a very, very deep sleep.

The craft is purposefully built without view holes so that no out-siders can breach them and so that the remnants will be spared from witnessing the death and destruction that is about to take place. The upper deck of the vessel has a built-in, fold-out ceiling that is to remain bolted shut until the Voice tells them it is safe to unbolt it and swing it open. With a heavy heart, CEO calls forth the hydrogen and oxygen atoms again, only this time there is no joy attached to the event.

When it first starts to rain, the remaining crowds outside head for higher ground and hunker down under the few nearby trees they are able to locate in the dark. Favored's satellite ON is not reflecting the light from Fun this night. As the canopy of water envelopes the orb, the blackness of night increases and shuts out the light from all the stars above. It is pitch black outside, and the crowds realize that their camping experience is turning nasty. As the waters begin to rise, many orblings remember what Comfort told them and in their panic try to blindly scramble back to the Refuge. Few find the way, and most are washed aside by the rushing waters. Those who do, desperately try to climb up the sides, pounding and screaming. But the family inside is in a deep sleep and cannot hear anything above the din of the relentless rain. The wood surfaces become very slick, and all the climbers lose their grip, slip off, and drown. Safely surrounded by the thick walls, the family and all the creatures inside sleep peacefully that night and cannot hear the faint and distant screams of the dying all around them. The water rises steadily throughout the night. By morning light, the Refuge is floating. Water keeps rising for another 39 orb days and nights until every high mountain is completely covered. The Refuge simply rises with the water and floats along safely.

When all land life outside the Refuge has perished, CEO ceases

His summoning and joining of hydrogen and oxygen atoms, and ends the surge. Completely covered in water, the orb creates the first prismatic event separating white light into the colors of the spectrum. The ensuing colored bands of light arcing across the orb sky, although very beautiful, reveal another first in the Universe—the splitting of light.

The Voice now tells Comfort and his family to push open the hinged ceiling of the craft and let the light in until they safely land on solid ground. After 150 orb days and nights, the ground of Favored is at last beginning to absorb the voluminous floodwaters. A few more orb months pass, and the water begins to subside. Containment has been achieved.

However, although Traitor and his cohorts were able to fly away and leave, their hybrid offspring could not, and thus, they perished in the surge. In the meantime, CEO set up a sterilization field in space that the Castaways had to pass through in order to escape Favored's deluge. Those who had found a way to make themselves reproductive were now rendered sterile by the CIA. Comfort, his family, and all the remaining animals are now able to resume their lives. CEO tells the family of Comfort to be fruitful and repopulate the orb. *"The fear of you and the terror of you shall be on every beast of the orb and on every bird of the sky, with everything that creeps on the ground, and all the fish of the sea. Into your hand they are given. Teach your children to heed my Voice, for it will be their strength and show them the way."*

PUSHING THROUGH DARKNESS

The process of free will continues. CEO waits patiently for character cultivation to mature as the remaining generations will once again choose their ultimate destinies.

After numerous successions, many of the children stop listening to the Voice. Traitor with his buddies come back to inhabit Favored. After all, they still have legal authority, and continue to entice CEO's children to follow his voice and do unloving and sick things. With all the intelligence given to the offspring, a lot of them still somehow manage to find debauchery more appealing than goodness. CEO, calm and confident, resting in His ceremonial chair at Headquarters tells His remaining faithful Secret Agents, *"I use the darkness! I use the dirt! They are My growth medium. Now we wait for the good crop—the fruit of our labor of love."* And all the Agents marvel over His wisdom.

A remnant of Comfort's generation is faithful to the Voice and brings Him hope and joy, especially the generations of Fame, Comfort's first-born son. Ally, who comes out of the successions of Fame, continues in his faithfulness to the Voice, and has a drop-dead gorgeous Assistant named Dominance. Ally and Dominance are faithful to CEO and live their lives accordingly. When the Voice speaks, they listen and do what He says. CEO takes note of them, and one day His Voice says to Ally, *"Take your Assistant and leave your homeland, your family, and your relatives and go to the land which I will show you, and I will make you a great land of people. I will favor those who favor you and I will condemn those who condemn you."* So Ally goes forth with his Assistant Dominance, as the Voice commanded.

The Voice tells them that they will have a son whose children's children will eventually create a great country. Ally and Dominance are now around 80 orb years old and have lived in the land of Camptown for ten years. They are still childless. As faithful as they have been to heed the Voice, they show signs of doubting the things CEO has told them. Ally has richly prospered, just as the Voice had spoken, and is quite wealthy. Many customs and traditions have been accepted by the generations which are not part of CEO's original plan, but nevertheless affect even his favorite remnants. Having been told she would bear a son, Dominance is anxious to make it happen, especially at her age. With their wealth, they are able to purchase a maid among the Gypsies living around Camptown to help Dominance with the daily chores of life. Her name is Murmur. She is much younger and stronger than Dominance and somewhat attractive. Dominance observes Ally checking her out and Murmur flirting with him. This bothers Dominance a little, but then it gives her an idea. She wants to have a child just like CEO has said. But when it doesn't happen on her time schedule, she grows impatient. When she repeatedly fails to conceive naturally, she decides she will have a child one way or the other, and finds a way to make it happen.

DOMINANCE CAUSES MURMUR'S IMPRUDENCE

Over dinner one evening, Dominance tells Ally that they could have a son with the help of Murmur. She is young and strong, and he could have sex with her just this one time in order to conceive. Murmur is consulted and thinks it is a great idea. She is privately scheming to get out of the maid business. And after all, even though Ally is old, he is a very rich man. She figures she'll be set for life. And this time, instead of double checking the matter with CEO, Ally lets his sex drive settle the matter. After Murmur starts showing her pregnancy, she begins to gloat in the presence of Dominance and taunt her. Dominance soon realizes that her idea was not a good one. Nevertheless, she is looking forward to having a son with Ally. Nine orb months later, Murmur gives birth to a healthy boy. The Voice tells Ally to name him Imprudence.

For eight orb years, Ally enjoys watching the boy grow up and becomes very fond of him. However, the gals are not getting along. Murmur's plans to oust Dominance are not working. Although Ally had sex with her to conceive, he still loves Dominance, and even though Dominance is old she is still a knockout, and Ally's first true love. Murmur stops working altogether and demands to be waited on. She now spends all her energy conniving ways to put a wedge of misery between Dominance and Ally. As the boy Imprudence grows up, Murmur feeds him with lies and hatred for Dominance. Under Murmur's hateful influence, Imprudence grows up resenting his stepmother, and she now feels his contempt as well. Nevertheless, Ally loves his son. He grows strong and becomes very athletic, which pleases his father very much. Murmur continues to poison her son's mind toward Dominance, and together they cause her to feel unwelcome and excluded in her own home. Instead of being part of a peaceful family, they divide it.

The Voice tells Ally that he and Dominance will give birth to a son of their own, as they have been originally foretold, even though they are now nearly 100 orb years old. This son is going to be the son of promise that CEO told them about. He will receive an everlasting contractual agreement from UF for himself and his successions. CEO has found a faithful people He is pleased with and through which He can work out His Restoration Plan. The Voice tells Ally that He has renamed him, and from this orb day forth, he will be called Faithful. He tells Faithful that He also renamed Dominance and that she will now be called Queen. The Voice tells them to heed His instructions and that they have found favor with their UF. Their prosperity will be expanded, and the land in which they now are visitors will be given to their son and his offspring as an everlasting contractual gift. Soon after, Dominance becomes pregnant. And lo and behold they have a son, and they name him Promise because he is the promised son.

Imprudence cannot handle losing all the attention that has been lavished upon him for the past 13 years and refuses to acknowledge the place and value of his half brother. Up to now, he has been treated as a son and heir, but this late arrival of his brother makes him and his future feel more than shaky. His name, life, and position are bound up in a conflict between two jealous Assistants. And rather than choose to love and accept his new brother, he makes a free will choice to hate him and create more division in the family.

At his brother Promise's weaning celebration, Queen catches Imprudence taunting his younger brother. This is the last straw for her. After thirteen years of crying and being emotionally abused, Queen tells Faithful she can't take it any more. The Voice tells Faithful to listen to Queen in order to keep peace. He also tells Faithful that Promise is to be his true heir and from his lineage will come the "selected" people. Murmur and her son Imprudence are to be sent away in order to return peace to their home. The Voice will guide both of them to safety and help them begin a new life in a distant land.

Faithful is saddened over having to lose Imprudence but tells Queen what the Voice has spoken and that she should do what she feels is necessary. Although tired of being mistreated and ostracized by her maid and stepson, Queen takes her time to make this difficult decision and ponders the consequences. With a heavy heart, she ultimately realizes that Murmur's heart has hardened and will not bend to allow healing or improved relations. Murmur taunts Queen once again and causes yet another heated exchange within the family. Emboldened by her conversation with Faithful, Queen finally snaps. She has had enough! She grabs Murmur by the hair and throws her out yelling, "You are fired and no longer welcome here!"

Murmur looks to Faithful for help, but he shakes his head and says, "You have disrespected Queen once too often, and though I am fond of you, I cannot help you now. You were supposed to help Queen, but you have done nothing but hurt and antagonize her." Completely unapologetic, Murmur calls Imprudence, angrily grabs him by the hand, and flees from the presence of Faithful and Queen. She tries to find her way back to the Land of the Gypsies from where she came. In His love and concern for both of them, the Voice helps guide them till they reach safety.

FIRST REPENTANCE

A saddened Faithful now turns back to UF, realizing things have gone very wrong. He has lost his firstborn, Imprudence, and everything seems to be a mess. CEO loves him because he reflects upon his actions and, although not perfect, tries to learn and do better. He is loving, kind and teachable, and he always comes back to the Voice. Faithful promises UF that he will listen to His Voice from this orb day forward and that he is truly sorry.

Just as CEO planned, free will is accomplishing the delineation and revelation of character in the generations of His Heirs. Signs of gratefulness, responsibility, maturity, and goodness are beginning to emerge and grow in a remnant. CEO has found a pedigree through which He will work His Restoration Plan. But before He can do so, He wants to test this subject one more time.

Faithful has purposed to always follow the Voice in the future, regardless of whether it feels good and even regardless of whether it makes sense to him. He has come to a place where he totally trusts UF and knows that no matter what, He always has his best interests at heart. However, what Faithful does not know is that UF is about to sorely try him one more time. A dark medium once again will be employed.

Faithful has resided in the Land of Seven Wells for quite some time when the Voice calls to him and says, *"Take your son Promise, whom you love, and go to the Hill Country. When you get there, I want you to take his life and give him back to Me."* Faithful goes forth and follows the Voice. He certainly does not understand this! His beloved son, given to him in his later years, who was promised to bring forth more successions than the stars in the sky, is now to be cut down and returned to UF. Many thoughts race through his mind, but he directs his heart to obey nevertheless. He knows that UF can bring Promise back to life or do anything else He wants. At the site in the Hill Country that he is guided to by The Voice, without hesitation, he is about to offer up his beloved son Promise.

Meanwhile, the Voice has sent a trusted Secret Agent ahead to stop Faithful as soon as he has passed this sore test. The Agent of the Voice tells him that his son Promise is to be spared and then relays His message: *"UF swears that because you have obeyed and not withheld your son, I will surely favor you and make your successions as numerous as the stars in the sky, and through your offspring all the peoples of this orb will be benefited."* Then Faithful and Promise return to the Land of Seven Wells. The Voice has now revealed to His Heirs a major clue of His upcoming Restoration Plan.

Queen lives to be 127 years old before she expires. Faithful is in a foreign land at the time, looking for a place to bury his beloved, departed Assistant. Because of CEO's promises, he finds favor with the strangers, and they offer to help him, for his reputation is above reproach and he is well respected. They sell him a field at a good price where he may bury his Assistant.

THE COMPLETION OF PROMISE

At 40 years old, Promise is ready and yearning to take an Assistant for himself, but there are no suitable candidates in the land where they live. His father Faithful sends one of his servants to the old country, among his relatives. There he hopes they will find a suitable Voice-heeding Assistant. Although UF tells him that the land of Camptown will ultimately be given to him and his successions, Faithful does not want his son to take an Assistant from among the gypsies there, for they do not listen to the Voice. In fact, they do not seek the UF at all. They admire the things He has made but do not want anything to do with the One who made them. Faithful does not want his son to take an Assistant from among the Voice shunners, lest his hearing also become impaired. Faithful's servant goes back to the old country and sets out to find his master's son an Assistant. CEO is so touched by this act of allegiance on the part of Faithful that He dispatches Strong Man to go before the servant to ensure the best selection.

Behind the scenes, Strong Man is covertly orchestrating the meeting. When the servant arrives just outside the City of Horseneigh with all his supplies and camels, he heads for the well, as he and his animals are very thirsty and tired from the long journey. There he meets a very beautiful young female who offers to water his camels. This is a lot of work with no foreseeable gain. The servant is touched and very grateful for her thoughtfulness, especially because he is exceedingly weary from his travels. When she finishes her gracious task, he thanks her by giving her several gold bracelets. She smiles and thanks him for the lovely, very unexpected and very valuable gifts. As she quickly puts them on her wrists, she notices that he appears exhausted. She also notices that he exudes an air of nobility and great warmth. Knowing that her mother is preparing a large roasted lamb this evening, more than enough to share, she asks him if he is in need of food and a place to rest. He answers yes and asks her where he might buy lodging.

Gazing upon her newly acquired bracelets, she knows that he has more than paid for dinner and lodging already. She continues to impress him with her kindness by offering him to lodge freely at her parent's home. She assures him that there is enough room in her parent's wood and mud house to accommodate him for the night, and there would be a place for his animals also. Needing rest and refreshment, he grate-fully accepts her invitation. Agent Strong Man speaks the Voice's will to the servant and tells him that this young female is the right one for his master's son.

Upon entering the house, the enticing smell of roasted, seasoned meat mingled with the aroma of freshly-baked bread smacks him in the nose, waking and rejuvenating him temporarily. Anticipating the won-derful home-cooked meal and upcoming restful night, he feels soothed, comforted, and refreshed already. The father leads him to a basin of water where he can wash. The family soon learns that he is the servant of distant relatives. Upon this discovery, a special wine is brought forth and opened in celebration of this wonderful meeting. They now truly welcome his visit and getting to hear news from afar.

Enjoying his dinner with the family that evening, he feels greatly refreshed and happy to share with them why he has come. As they are savoring the last of the wine and lamb, he tells them that his master is very wealthy and wants a suitable Assistant for his son and that there are none where they reside. He tells them that their daughter would be perfect for him. The parents are impressed with the servant and his demeanor and manners, and they give their approval, provided that Fetching, their daughter, agrees. As the delicious meal is concluding, Fetching is filled in by the servant about all of Promise's qualities. She listens wide-eyed and attentively about his kindness, his wonderful parents, and great wealth. The servant also tells her that he is as handsome as she is beautiful. By the time the fig tart and sweet dates are served and the last cup of tea has been consumed, Fetching agrees to go back with him to be with Promise. The servant now opens his pack and pulls out several gold necklaces and puts them around her neck. Then he places some golden rings with precious stones on her fingers. The family continues to celebrate the joyous occasion by pulling out a very special, reserved and sweet after-dinner wine. They toast each other and give thanks to their UF for every wonderful thing that has happened this night. And before they have finished the last of the tasty sweet wine, the servant bestows many valuable gold coins on the parents.

Noticing the servant's exhaustion from his long trip, the wonderful meal, the wine, and the celebration, Fetching's father shows their guest where he may sleep. Still enjoying the glow of all that has transpired, the Assistants muster up enough energy to clean up. Then all the candles are blown out, and everyone retires for needed rest. They visit together for several more days to give all of them time to say farewell. After about a week, Fetching reluctantly bids her family goodbye and leaves with the servant, exhilarated about her upcoming new life and finally getting to meet Promise.

The long trip is at last over as the camels and the servant return to the land where Faithful and his son Promise reside. Seeing the procession of camels coming in the distance, Promise runs out to meet it. He acknowledges the servant and immediately looks for the girl and checks her out. As soon as his eyes meet hers and he looks her over, a huge smile appears on his face. Immediately captured by her beauty, he helps her off the camel. She is impressed. Promise gives the servant a strong hug, and they all head for the shelter of the tents. While they wash up, another servant attends to the needs of the animals. Supper is served shortly afterwards, and while they eat and drink together, everyone is getting acquainted. Clearly the young couple is emotionally, spiritually, intellectually, and physically well matched. Everyone heartily approves of Fetching, and she is very happy to be with them, and especially with Promise. It appears quite evident to everyone that they are both smitten with each other. Shortly thereafter, the formal unification ceremony is conducted. Everyone is celebrating the happy occasion. Promise is consoled over the loss of his beloved mother Queen through his new love and Assistant. Faithful gives Promise Queen's tent to dwell in with his new Assistant. His sad days are now replaced with the joy he shares with Fetching.

After Queen's death, Faithful takes another Assistant named Incense and lives to be 175 years old and then expires. For the purpose of burying their father, the sons of Faithful come together again for the first time since Murmur was thrown out and took Imprudence with her. He is laid to rest next to his first Assistant, Queen, in the field purchased for her. The offspring Faithful had while with his last Assistant, Incense, are given money and gifts, but they are ultimately sent away. Imprudence is left with only some token gifts, which leaves him once again feeling rebuffed by his birth father. Coming to help bury his father, he had hoped that there might be some serious inheritance for him. Only his son Promise, whom he had with his Assistant, Queen, is given the bulk family inheritance. Deep anger inside Imprudence's heart has been smoldering for years but is now rekindled from his unmet expectations. He allows his hatred for his half-brother to escalate to new heights, and he spits on both the graves of Faithful and Queen before he leaves. The Voice, however, knowing the propensities of the inner heart, had confirmed that the inheritance would fall to Promise even before he was born and that from his generations would emerge CEO's selected people.

THE SUPPLANTING

Fetching has the same problem as her deceased mother-in-law—difficulty conceiving. She and Promise have been together for twenty years, and they still are not able to have a child. Promise petitions UF daily to let Fetching bear children. UF has always taught His selected people that petitions are the ultimate wireless connection to their UF. Finally their petitions are answered, and Fetching at last is pregnant. She and Promise look forward to having their own child, but as her pregnancy progresses, she experiences a tremendous amount of pain and kicking. She tells Promise that it feels like a war is literally going on inside her womb. The severe movement and kicking continues until the very last day before delivery. After such an extremely difficult pregnancy, they are both anticipating the birth of their first child with trepidation. Promise is petitioning UF for the life of his Assistant. He longs for his child but does not want to lose Fetching. And Promise has to reassure Fetching often that all will be well, despite her difficult pregnancy. The Voice speaks to both of them as He tells Fetching, *"Two nations inside of you are about to be birthed. One will be stronger than the other. And the firstborn will serve the second."*

After many hours of difficult labor, Fetching finally delivers a baby. The head appears, then the arms, and once the legs appear the gender is revealed. It is a beautiful boy. But the foot of the firstborn has a little hand attached to it. And soon another boy is delivered right on the heels of the first. The parents are amazed at their two little miracles. Both appear healthy and whole, except that the second-born has a lot of bruises on him. The parents assume that he was bruised while coming through the birth canal. Fetching has come through safely, although she is completely worn out. They name the firstborn twin Red, because even as a baby he bears a shock of red hair. The second-born twin is named Grasp, because he was grasping onto his brother's heel when he was born. CEO has been carefully observing his pedigree. The parents faintly hear The Voice speak, *"Grasp I love, and Red I despise."* The incredibly harsh statement, coupled with their faint hearing and fatigue, causes them to brush it aside. For now, they just want to enjoy their boys and each other.

As the two young boys grow up, Promise takes a special liking to Red. He is hairy, rough, and outdoorsy. He skillfully learns to hunt game and enjoys doing lots of things with his father that require heavy lifting. Because Promise loves the outdoors and hunting as well, they get on nicely. Grasp, on the other hand, is not as strong as his brother and doesn't like to hunt, so he stays closer to the home tents and helps his mother with many of the household chores. He hauls water and carries supplies. He tends the animals and helps his mother with the cooking. He is willing to help with anything and everything, but he hates to hunt game, though he always cleans and prepares it. He also loves to read and write. Fetching loves this son because he is very thoughtful. Besides being helpful, he is also very intelligent, well read, well mannered, kind, and polite.

Red and Grasp are alone in the kitchen part of the tent. Red has been out on a long hunt and has brought home more game. Grasp spent the day making carpets and clothing out of skins. He prepared the game his brother brought home and then made a savory stew and baked several loaves of bread to last for the next few days. The aroma fills the tent and drives his brother Red crazy. Dinner is going to be served in another hour, and the whole family will sit down together and eat, as customary. Red does not want to wait and insists on getting a bowl of stew immediately. Grasp reminds him that dinner is now only a half hour away from being served to everyone. Red is a carnal man who always insists on getting what he wants when he wants it. He glibly tells Grasp he will trade his inheritance for a bowl of stew now. Not believing his ears, Grasp turns to face his brother, and asks, "Are you serious?" And Red once again glibly says, "Yeah, what good is my inheritance if I'm starving?"

It is now only fifteen minutes before dinner. In his gut, Grasp knows that Red stole his inheritance in the womb because of his superior strength, and he also stole his father's heart the same way. He decides to take Red to task. "Very well, if you think so little of our family's inheritance that you would trade it away for a bowl of stew, I will oblige you, as long as you swear to our UF that I may have your inheritance." "Yeah, yeah, I swear. Now give me the darn stew." Shaking his head, Grasp attempts to hand the bowl to his brother, but it is rudely ripped out of his hands. Red lustily grabs the stew and wolfs it down. Then he joins the family fifteen minutes later to eat again. After consuming more stew, bread, and wine, he finally passes out. When he wakes up, he spends the rest of the evening recounting tales of his hunting adventures to his father outside under the light of the stars. He leaves Grasp to help their mother clean up in the kitchen.

As the young men grow into adults, the parents retain and solidify their prejudices. Promise still favors Red over Grasp. When he reaches his last days, Promise wants to give the family inheritance to his firstborn, as is the usual custom. He has long chosen to forget what the Voice told him and Fetching at the time the boys were born—that the boys would both father nations and that the firstborn, in this case, would serve the second. UF knows what happened in the womb, something the parents could not see. A war was fought to supplant the true firstborn. Red possessed superior strength over his brother, even when they were forming in the womb. He used that strength to shove, kick, punch, and push his brother around in the embryonic sac until he was out of the way, so that he could be born first. Fully aware of this fact and so much more about the two brothers, CEO had expressed His opinion to the parents through the Voice. Many times UF has spoken to Promise that "*Grasp I love, and Red I hate.*" But Promise's love for Red dulls his hearing. Both brothers are now fully grown, and Promise is about to give the family inheritance to Red. Fetching is unable to persuade Promise otherwise. Totally frustrated, she takes matters into her own hands. Promise is very old, and his vision has grown quite dim. He can make out only shadows. His days are numbered, and he intends to get the family business in order.

Fetching tells Grasp that he must do exactly as she says. Promise is waiting for Red to come back from another outing of hunting game. She is aware that this night is when he plans on giving Red the family inheritance. Red is due back shortly. After he spends hours in the woods hunting, he rarely washes up. Instead he smacks on some pungent coriander oil to mask his odor. He buys the oil from traders, who pick it up from the Land of Kermit. Fetching doesn't like the smell, but since Promise has lost most of his vision, he likes it; it helps him unmistakably sense when his favorite son is around. Grasp can't stand the smell and has never worn it. Fetching tells Grasp to splash some of the coriander oil on himself and go in to see his father and pretend he is

Red. As Grasp enters the room, Promise smells the coriander and proceeds to give Grasp the family's inheritance. Only twenty minutes later, Red, slathered in coriander oil, walks in to see his father. Promise's nose tells him Red has come back. He jokingly asks him, "Do you not think it's enough?" Red replies, "What are you talking about father?" Promise says, "The inheritance I just gave you?" Red says, "What inheritance, I just walked in?" Now shaken, Promise calls Fetching and Grasp. Grasp is scared, but Fetching calms him and says, "I will take the heat." They enter the room, and Promise demands an explanation.

Fetching tells Promise that Red chose to trade away his inheritance to his brother for a mere bowl of stew. He did this while swearing an oath before UF. And Fetching reminds Promise of the Voice's decree at their birth about who was going to serve whom. Realizing that his prejudicial love for Red has clouded his hearing, he begins to weep. His heart has always wanted it be the other way around. However, the siftings of life have at last settled the matter. Not willing to give it up, Red pleads with his father to fix this, but with tears in his eyes, Promise sadly tells Red that the matter is now out of his hands. Strong willed and rarely losing at anything due to his brute strength, Red turns toward Grasp. If looks could kill, his icy stare would have done the job.

There is no spirited conversation at dinner that evening. Grasp serves everyone, and Red continues to glare at him. He finishes every last bite of the roasted venison, which should have lasted several more days, eats two loaves of bread and drinks the remainder of the wine from a newly-opened full skin. Then, as he often does, he passes out and goes into a heavy sleep.

Late that evening, Fetching pulls Grasp aside and whispers some instructions to him. Fearing for his life, she tells him to get up before dawn and leave their home until Red's fury is spent and he has sufficient time to cool off. After explaining to him how to get to her brother's house in the distant city of Horseneigh, she hands him a prepared travel pack and kisses him goodbye. "Red has no knowledge of my brother or where he lives," says Fetching. "Go quickly before first light and may UF be with you." Knowing his brother all too well, Grasp sees this is a good plan and kisses his mother goodbye. He then goes in to see his father. Neither exchanges any words, but Grasp kisses his father on the forehead and then grabs a few hours of sleep before departing on his long journey.

At first light, Red awakens from his drunken stupor, and as he rubs the morning grit from his eyes, his brain fog begins lifting. The early light shines some clarity on his memory of what happened the night before. He remembers why he ate and drank too much. He was trying to avoid the temptation of attacking his brother in front of his father. But he was scheming to beat the crap out of him the very first chance he got. In fact, murder had even crossed his mind. After washing up, getting dressed, and grabbing a bite to eat, he heads outside hoping to catch Grasp hauling water or tending to the animals. He is re-energized by the thought of setting the record straight and getting even. Used to getting what he wants, he wasn't going to let a small technicality like having traded away his inheritance for a bowl of stew stop him. He would make his brother hand it over, or he would beat it out of him. After all, he had done a similar thing to him while they were both still in the womb.

After searching everywhere, he is unable to find Grasp. He goes inside and asks his mother in a rather uncharacteristically polite manner, "Where may I find my brother?" Knowing this son, and suspecting his polite demeanor is just a put on, she answers him ever so sweetly, "He was just watering the animals." Without acknowledging his mother, he races outside to where the animals are, but he finds no Grasp. After searching for him all day and questioning both his mother and father to no avail, he begins to realize that his brother has fled from home. Having no target for his wrath, he grabs his bow and arrow with a fiend-like vengeance, in search of one. After several hours, he comes back with a very unlucky deer.

GRASPING FOR NEW DIGS

When Grasp finally reaches the outskirts of the City of Horseneigh, he is tired and hungry. He finds three large flocks of sheep with shepherds tending them. A young woman with one of the flocks looks at him curiously. He is immediately captivated by her physical beauty. He asks her if she knows a man named Whitey. "Why do you want to know?" she asks him. He answers, "My mother is his sister, and I have come a very long way." She smiles and says, "I am his daughter Ewenice, and will take you to him." So happy to find his kin, he hugs and kisses her.

When Ewenice brings Grasp home to meet Whitey, smiles abound. They are delighted to meet distant kin, and they let him wash up and then comfortably settle on pillows inside the house to catch up on all the history of their families. While sharing, they are visited by delicious smells that tell them dinner is almost ready. The Assistants take turns entering the conversation while finalizing the meal preparations. Wine is poured and toasts are shared. Earlier that day, the Assistants stuffed a large leg of lamb with breadcrumbs, cinnamon, lemon slices, and garlic cloves. They then perfectly glazed it with the puree of lemon, more garlic, more cinnamon, and ginger oil. Seasoned wild rice is now tender and is topped with grapes and nuts. Lots of small sautéed onions finish the greens. The efforts are now paying off as the magnificent aromas are teasing everyone. Wild blueberries picked earlier in the day have also made it possible to present a sweet pie finish. While savoring the final bite of his pie and leisurely sipping the last of his tea, Grasp is fascinated by Ewenice. He is drawn to her fiery eyes and physical beauty. They have gravitated toward each other throughout the meal. After dinner, they all share a short stroll under the stars before everyone is ready to call it a night. Whitey shows Grasp where he may sleep. He is tired, but he feels good as he lays his head down. He is safe, warm, and completely satisfied for now.

The next morning, Grasp tells Whitey that he would like to work for him and stay a while. Having no sons to help him, Whitey really likes the idea of having a strapping young man around to help. "I am very fond of Ewenice," Grasp says. "I would like to have her for my Assistant." Whitey is quiet for a moment and then replies, "It is not customary or right that my second-born Ewenice is given away before my firstborn. I would like you to take Hefferina, Ewenice's sister, for your Assistant. She is a gentle soul. Her eyes may not have the fire that Ewenice's have, but they have a kindly tenderness. Although she is not as beautiful in form as her younger sister, she is strong and will work hard and bear you many children." Totally smitten by the fiery Ewenice, Grasp completely dismisses Whitey's words of protocol and tells him that he is fond of Ewenice, not Hefferina. "And I believe that she is fond of me as well," says Grasp. Not unlike his brother Red, he now wants what he wants when he wants it. He can't see past his desire. Instead of taking his time, he hastily chooses. Then he offers, "I will work for you for seven years if you will give me Ewenice." He thought, *This is such a high price to pay, surely Whitey cannot refuse.* Indeed, Whitey reluctantly agrees, not able to pass up such a deal.

Grasp is so happy to be near Ewenice he hardly notices the seven years he has spent working for Whitey. Holding her hand and strolling with her after dinners, discussing their future plans together all have made the time fly by. Their ceremonial day is upon them. They are both eager and excited to be formally united at long last. They have planned for this day for many years. Their passions completely aflame, they can hardly wait to have each other unreservedly.

At the unification celebration everyone is having a grand time. The celebration has been going all day, and the family and guests are winding down. Delicious food was served all day long, and the wine is still flowing. As dusk creeps over the gathering, guests who came from nearby begin to leave. Those who came from greater distances pitch tents and bed down for the night.

SECOND SUPPLANTING

Whitey always had second thoughts after he agreed to this arrangement. He has been scheming on how to weasel out of the deal for a very long time. He really doesn't want to give up his younger daughter before the elder. Hefferina is not as beautiful as Ewenice, and Whitey is afraid she will never be united. Everyone has had a lot of wine, and they are all happy and very mellow. Whitey has also had a lot of wine, which loosens his inhibitions and blots his conscience. He feels brazen enough to execute a scheme he has been hatching in his heart and mind. He calls some of his servants over to help him. Then he strolls over to Ewenice, who is beside Grasp, and puts his arm around his daughter. He tells Grasp he needs to borrow her for a little while in order to share some final words of wisdom with her. Grasp kisses her and tells her to hurry back.

It is dark now, and they are both eagerly awaiting a night of bliss in their own tent. The family and friends have decorated their tent beautifully, with all manner of fine linens and pillows. They have included a lovely bowl filled with fresh fruit for morning, as well as an assortment of gourds filled with water, fresh fruit juices, and more wine. She kisses him back, wraps her arms around her father, and happily walks off with him. The servants meet them with torches to light their path in the dark. Ewenice thanks her father for the beautiful party he has provided. They keep walking until they reach some camels off in the distance. Then they sit down on a blanket, where they are served some extra-strong wine. Whitey tells his daughter to drink up because he has something important he wants to tell her. After she finishes two cups, she is barely coherent. He tells his servants to take her to a tent he had them set up earlier. The female servants assigned to the tent are to keep her safe there until morning. She has had enough wine to dull her wit and senses and make her very sleepy. When they bring her inside, she eagerly heads for the bedding and lies down. Once her head hits the pillow, she falls asleep.

Whitey now finds an inebriated Hefferina. She has been drinking to drown her sorrows for not being chosen while her younger sister has found love. It was truly embarrassing for the older daughter not to be united first. He puts frankincense and myrrh on her neck and the inside of her wrists. Then he walks her in the direction of Grasp's tent. He tells her that Grasp has a change of heart. "He expressed his preference for you this last hour," says Whitey. "He asked me to give you to him instead of Ewenice. They had a terrible, irreconcilable fight. Ewenice is so angry with Grasp for changing his mind that she stormed off in a huff and left with one of our guest families. It is OK for him to change his mind, as long as he does it before they have sex." Hefferina is flattered, though totally perplexed. She has always wanted Grasp, but lost out to her sister. "Grasp is in his tent, lonely and hoping that you will come and consummate the unification ceremony with him. He is longing for you," Whitey tells her. Her father now orders her to sleep with Grasp, thereby legally uniting the two of them. The customs of their day allow the fathers to dictate the lives of the daughters.

That being said, Hefferina, filled with strong wine and passions, is really not thinking too clearly. Before she really knows what is happening, the strong arm of her father drags her along until they are in front of Grasp's tent. Opening the tent flap, he just about throws her inside. As she stumbles in the darkness she falls into the arms of Grasp. Having waited so long for his beloved, Grasp now hurries to have her. Whitey made sure earlier that no implements of light were allowed into the ceremonial tent. Receiving Grasp's warm reception and passionate advances, she stops thinking altogether and succumbs to the moment. Filled with drink and giddy passions, they make love over and over in the dark of night, in the seclusion of the tent. After listening for some-time, and realizing his plan has worked beautifully, Whitey walks back to his house with a smile on his face.

THE MOURNING AFTER

Morning comes, and with it the light of day. Hefferina is lying in bed next to Grasp while he is cuddled up to her back. She is in a euphoric state from the night before. She can hardly believe she is united with Grasp. She was beginning to think she would never taste the passions of lovemaking. Her sexuality fully awakened and stirred, she feels desired and more complete. When Grasp awakens, he kisses her back and tenderly reaches for her. He can't wait to see her and gaze into her fiery eyes for the first time since their night of passion. She turns around to face him and kiss him back, but he finds the soft, tender eyes of Hefferina instead. He jumps up in shock, gasping. "What is this?" he fairly screams. Hefferina's warm, loving gaze now turns into a frightful look. The wheels in her head are turning and clicking. Thoughts run through her mind about what her father told her. In a flash, she realizes what has been done. She had been tricked into believing that Grasp had chosen her, and Grasp had been tricked into believing he had been given Ewenice. The sanitizing truth of morning light immediately turns her newfound joy and bliss into sorrow, and she starts to weep inconsolably, realizing that all his love and passion were really not for her.

Grasp gets dressed, leaving Hefferina in tears, and heads outside to seek Whitey. He runs to the house, and upon finding him sipping hot tea while eating breakfast, demands an explanation. Content with himself for having skillfully killed two birds with one stone, so to speak, Whitey looks up with a smile on his face. "It is the custom and the appropriate thing to do," he calmly and smugly informs Grasp. "If you will honor Hefferina during your ceremonial week of unification, I will give you Ewenice the following week. Then you will have both of them for your own! But you must work for me another seven years." Aching and longing to have Ewenice and having to wait just one more week for her, Grasp agrees to the arrangement.

To say Grasp is livid is an understatement. He now seeks to know Ewenice's whereabouts. A servant leads him to her in a distant tent. She is awake, but is throwing up from all the stiff drink she had the night before. She looks up at him, knowing in her gut that something is terribly wrong. He looks at her, and tears stream down his face. He hugs her, and then walks away in grief. She spends most of the rest of the day trying to get well. The week goes by before the three of them come to grips with what has been done to them. The two sisters must make amends and find a way to deal with the situation. Grasp knows he must also honor Hefferina, and Ewenice is deeply disturbed by the arrangement. It goes without saying that the stunt Whitey pulled on them causes a great rift in the family. None of the duped find him beloved or trustworthy any longer.

When Grasp fulfills his week with Hefferina, he is given Ewenice. They are thrilled to be together at long last, but their relationship is fraught with complications. These seven years do not fly by as before. They feel cumbersomely long. Hefferina, unlike her sister Ewenice, is extremely fertile and bears Grasp children every year. She is pregnant during the entire seven years. She gives him six sons, each time hoping that maybe now he will come to love her. Although he cares, his heart has always belonged to Ewenice. However, Ewenice has trouble conceiving. She now feels desperate for a child and starts blaming Grasp, yelling at him for impregnating her sister and not her. Tensions between them grow. Her sister is pregnant with her seventh child before Ewenice is finally able to conceive. Hefferina gives birth to her seventh child, a girl, just before Ewenice gives birth to her first. Grasp and his growing family stay with Whitey a few more years to build up their flocks of sheep and camels. Ewenice at last gives birth to her first child who is a son, and they name him Increase. Both Ewenice and Grasp feel happy, relieved, and fulfilled to finally have birthed a child from their love.

Having paid his debt to Whitey, built up his flocks and family, and with the last two pregnancies birthed safely, Grasp instructs his two Assistants to ready everyone for travel. The gals pack up what is theirs and prepare their children for departure. Hefferina and Ewenice are equally anxious to get away from their scheming father. Grasp now gathers his family, his personal possessions, and his flocks and shakes the dust off his sandals as he leaves the house of Whitey and the City of Horseneigh.

SEEING RED

During the years Grasp is away, Red takes a lot of his anger out on his parents by pricking their ire. He blames the loss of his inheritance on everyone but himself. His parents do not approve of the Assistants residing in and around Camptown. He not only takes several of these as his own Assistants, but then goes off to the Plains of the Highlands to seek a few more from the descendants of Imprudence. This really upsets his parents because the Imprudents are known for being an angry, wild people.

LAST STRAW

After three days, Whitey, with a huge escort, intercepts and meets up with Grasp and his daughters. He is intent on stopping them. He claims they have stolen valuable golden implements from his household when they departed. They are lucky charms he uses in prayer. CEO considers such to be idols and despises their use. Instead of seeking the Voice, these orblings believe material things have the power to hear. They rub the objects, thinking they are what bring them luck and blessings. Once they believe that, the next step isn't far behind: They begin to worship the idol itself. Traitor has spread these deceptions around, and many orblings have bought into the false traditions. Traitor loves it when the Heirs buy his lies and he can lead them astray. Even some Voice heeders foolishly buy into these deceptive customs.

Grasp is furious, not just at the accusation but that his father-in-law is worshiping idols. He looks at Whitey and says, "I have faithfully worked for you for 14 years, even though you have cheated me many times. I have not taken one thing from your household that is not mine. I want nothing to do with idols and will not have them in my midst." He then turns to his Assistants and his Assistants' attendants and asks, "Has anyone here taken anything that is not yours from Whitey?" All respond with a resounding "No." Therefore, Grasp confidently tells Whitey, "If you find anything that is yours, you may take it back. And so that you may know my sincerity, I swear by UF that whosoever stole your idols will be stricken down!" Whitey searches and searches, but he does not find his golden idols.

Unbeknownst to Grasp, Ewenice never forgave her father for the stunt he pulled and is also very angry at UF for not allowing her to conceive during the years her sister was constantly pregnant. One night she found her father's golden idols and started rubbing them for luck. When Increase was born, she just assumed they were the reason she got pregnant and did not give the glory to UF. Now that she is pregnant again and they are leaving, she had stolen them and hid them inside the camel's saddle upon which she sat. When her father is checking everything, she lies and tells him she cannot get up because it is her time of the month. Whitey finds nothing, and Grasp is insulted for the way he chased them down like hoodlums. Having been patient with his schemes and trickery all these years, he has had enough. Grasp's voice, filled with indignant boldness, blares out, "Now leave me and my household, and never bother me again!" Detecting the peeved tone of agitation in Grasp's voice, Whitey finally apologizes, kisses his daughters goodbye, and leaves, somewhat embarrassed.

SELECTED PEDIGREE CONTINUES

Twenty years after he fled from his brother Red, Grasp heads back through the Plains of the Highlands toward his father's home. With wives, children, sheep, camels, and some acquired possessions in tow, the journey now takes much, much longer. Ewenice is expecting her second child. On the way to a place in the country about twelve miles north of the City of Salem, Grasp has an encounter with his UF. CEO appears before Grasp. The Voice speaks, *"I will continue to prosper you. You will no longer be called Grasp. From this orb day forward your name shall be Prevail for you have prevailed well, in spite of having been supplanted twice. But it has all helped you to grow, even though you don't understand and see everything. You were named Grasp, and everyone thinks you are a supplanter, but I see the heart and its intentions! Your ways are not perfect, but your heart's intentions are true. From your successions will emerge nations and rulers. The land which I gave to your grandfather Faithful and your father Promise, I give to you and to your successions after you."* Then CEO beams Himself up into CIA's transporter and returns to Nucle-Eye Headquarters. Prevail names this spot in the country north of Salem, where UF benefited him and his successions, House of UF.

A little distance farther from there is the Town of Bread. But before they get to Bread, Ewenice goes into hard labor, and the difficult labor continues for hours. Frail as she is, her body expires after she delivers her second son. Prevail mourns and buries her between House of UF and the City of Bread and grieves her loss for a long time.

Prevail names his son Rightson, and eventually the pain of her death is replaced with the joy of watching him grow. Ewenice and Prevail had two sons, Increase and Rightson. Hefferina gave Prevail six sons: Sonsee, Earson, Joiner, Reward, Praise and Dwell. Hefferina also gave Prevail one daughter named Justine. These are the offspring of Prevail with his two Assistants.

Prevail continues on to the City of Friend, the land where he dwelled with his father Promise and his mother Fetching before he left to escape his brother's wrath. After a lengthy reunion with his son Prevail and his family and having lived a long full life, Promise finally expires at the age of 180 years. At this time, Red comes home to pay his respects and help his brother bury his father. So many years had gone by since he forfeited his inheritance that he no longer wants to kill his brother. After visiting and meeting each other's families, Red takes his tribe back to the Plains of the Highlands. Prevail stays with his family in the land where his father had lived.

THE VISION

Increase and Rightson are the sons of Prevail's old age and his youngest. They are the only two sons he had with his beloved Ewenice. Increase now almost seventeen, is definitely his father's favorite. The other brothers from Hefferina sense and feel the partiality. He receives visions from the BT and seems to even be favored by UF. His stepbrothers are jealous and allow resentment to grow in their hearts. One morning, Increase naively shares a dream he had the night before. Without realizing the consequences of his sharing a powerful revelation he was given by the BT, he wants to share it with his already envious elder siblings. Being so much younger and always dismissed by them, he seeks to impress them, and he wants them to help him confirm what he thinks it means. They do not receive dreams and visions.

Foolishly unaware that this will neither impress nor endear him to them, he excitedly begins to share. "I saw all of you, Rightson, and our father bow before me. You had traveled a great distance and came begging for food. I was adorned in fine clothes and jewelry and had the power of a great ruler. Were it not for my benevolence, none of you would have survived." They listened, and then they became very angry. "We are going to bow down to you! Really! Being father's favorite has truly gone to your head." They begin to laugh hysterically in his face. During dinner, they mockingly share his vision with their father,

124

and especially the part where Increase said that even *he* would bow down to him. Now Prevail is peeved. "Really, Increase, don't you think your imagination is getting a bit out of hand? Enough of this nonsense! I don't want to hear another word about this!" Chuckling and smirking, his half-brothers pass the bread and wine. They finally succeed in dropping Increase's esteem a notch in their father's eyes. Sharing his dream has not gone the way he hoped. No one is impressed. He sheepishly eats his roast of lamb and quietly sips a little wine to nurse his wounds.

His half-brothers drive their flocks of sheep to distant pastures, and now have been gone for several days. Concerned because they have been gone so long, Prevail sends Increase after them and asks him to report back on how they are doing and if everything is OK. Increase heads out the following morning and begins his search. He travels for several days until he finds them. The brothers see him coming from a distance and cringe. "Here comes daddy's favorite little boy!" "Here comes the one we are going to worship!" "Ha, ha!" they grumble, while feigning phony bows. They huddle together and conspire to kill him. "Let's get rid of him. Then we shall see what becomes of his dreams of grandeur! Besides, if we don't, he will probably inherit everything our father has." Overhearing this, Sonsee, the eldest, is deeply disturbed. He is not fond of Increase, but he does not want the transmission fluid of his younger stepbrother on his head. He also honors and fears UF's Voice. This just sounds too rotten to him. He suggests they throw him into a nearby pit but that no one lays a hand on him. He secretly plans in his mind to rescue him later, when the others aren't looking.

When Increase reaches them, he asks, "How's it going?" They don't answer; they just grab him. Wide-eyed and confused at what they are doing, he feels the sting and pain of being thrown into a pit. Before throwing him in, they strip him of his warm coat. Scratched and bruised, he shakes his head and looks up for mercy, but finds none. He cries, "Please help me out!" But all he hears is laughter and snickering. They sit down to eat their lunches of bread, fruit, and raisins. Sipping their tea, they smugly smile at each other. Realizing they are serious, he begins to weep. Hearing him cry, they mock him again.

Fully expecting to rescue him later, Sonsee is tending sheep off in the distance. The lunching brothers look up and see a caravan of camels coming toward them laden with gum, balm, and myrrh. The descendents of Imprudence are traveling with their trade to the Land of Kermit. Praise, Hefferina's fourth son, now tells his brothers, "Let's not kill him, just like Sonsee said earlier, and have that on our hands. Let's sell him as a slave to the Imprudents. They will take him far away, he will be a slave, and we will be rid of him!" They all think this is a brilliant idea. In addition, they make 20 silver coins from the deal. When Sonsee comes back late that afternoon hoping to rescue him, his brothers tell him what they have done. He nearly faints. "What have you done?" he screams. "What will we tell our father? He will be devastated." The brothers had already figured out how to cover their behinds. They had killed a goat from among the sheep and dipped Increase's coat into its transmission fluid and ripped it in several places. "We will take the coat to him and tell him that a wild animal must have grabbed him, and this is all that we were able to retrieve." Sonsee, shaken, scared, and trapped in the disaster, now can't think of anything else to do but go along with the lie. When the deceitful brothers finally make their way home, Earson and Joiner are, incredibly, stepping lighter. Feeling no remorse, they look forward to Increase's permanent absence.

All the brothers bring the transmission fluid soaked coat to their father Prevail. His eyes nearly pop out when he recognizes it. "What is this?" he asks, as he starts feeling his throat constrict and tears well up. The sons take turns responding. "This is all that is left of Increase. A wild animal must have grabbed him. He is surely dead." His tears now break loose like a flood, and Prevail begins to weep and shake uncontrollably. He mourns for a very long time, and even though all his remaining sons and daughters try to console him, nothing helps. Sonsee, overtaken by guilt and disgust, withdraws from his brothers and his father's house. He makes a home elsewhere and eventually starts his own family.

Increase arrives in the Land of Kermit in chains. From there he is sold to a high-ranking officer named African Bull. Everyone calls him AB for short. AB brings Increase into his household. UF is watching from Headquarters and causes everything that Increase touches or works on to be benefited or increased. AB begins to notice that there is something special about Increase and that his household has benefited greatly since his arrival. With each passing day, he trusts Increase with more and more responsibilities and duties that turn out beneficial for him.

AB is a middle-aged man who has a slightly younger Assistant. He is a nobleman in the community and keeps a very respectable household. But he is not aware of his Assistant's adulterous heart. Her name is, fittingly, Cougar. She is getting older and is having a hard time watching her beauty fade. She has great wealth, thanks to AB, and too much idle time on her hands. Instead of channeling or managing her time constructively, she lusts after other males, especially younger ones. Instead of appreciating what AB has provided for her, she disrespects him behind his back. The willing participants in her schemes do not honor UF or even care what they are doing to AB, assuming what he doesn't know won't hurt him.

Increase has grown into a handsome, strapping young man.

Cougar has been salivating over him for several months and dropping sexual hints whenever AB is not around. Increase avoids her like the plague, which really infuriates her. He is not responding to her schemes and advances. He is a slave in his master's house, and if he were to get caught he could be killed. Besides that, he doesn't want to dishonor his UF because he knows that is where all his benefits come from and ultimately where his deliverance will come from as well. His master has grown fond of him and trusts him with his entire household. Increase is too intelligent to mess it up.

When AB departs to a foreign land on business for many days, Cougar decides to make her move. She lies in wait to attack her unsuspecting prey. Increase has been working hard outside in the courtyards, making some construction changes that AB wants done while he is gone. Tired and in need of a bath, he heads for the bathhouse and soaks his weary muscles. He is in the process of drying off and getting dressed. He is not aware that Cougar has secretly sent all the other help to town on the pretense of errands so she can be alone with him. Heading for the bathhouse, she makes her move. She enters while he is still dressing. Her inappropriate behavior sets off his internal alarm, and he attempts to quickly finish dressing and makes a mad dash to escape. She tries to seduce him and grabs his cloak, but he runs like a gazelle. He runs so fast from her that she is left with his cloak in her hands. He hides until she gives up searching. No one has ever refused her before, least of all a slave. Her ego is bruised by his rebuffing her, and her anger simmers until it reaches a full-throttle boil. She does not want to ever see or face again the one who had the nerve to reject her. She intends to get even!

When AB returns home, she runs to him crying. "I have been raped by your slave! While everyone was gone from the house, he took advantage of me, and here is his cloak for proof." AB is grieved and torn. There are no witnesses but Cougar and Increase. He summons Increase and interrogates him. Increase swears by his UF to AB that he never touched his Assistant, but Cougar swears that he raped her. AB has no choice but to take the word of his Assistant over that of his slave and avenge her, even though he has grown fond of Increase. With a heavy heart he sends Increase to prison, and the benefits his household received from above cease.

Not only a slave, Increase is now a prisoner, and he feels hopeless beyond words, having been ripped from his family, with no help in sight, cheated out of his inheritance, and now a lowly slave in prison. It takes every fiber in him not to weep bitterly in front of the others. But he realizes that is dangerous; there is no pity for crybabies in the hole he is in. He had been doing so well at AB's house, earning privileges and some comforts. He had been careful to honor his master, but in the end he was falsely accused by Cougar.

Increase turns to the only source of strength left to him, his UF. Petitioning him daily for help and listening for the Voice's direction, he clings to his only hope. Before long, miracles seem to happen for him again. His hard work and diligence pay off, and he is put in charge of other prisoners. The prison warden takes a liking to him, and whatsoever is done there, he is put in charge of it.

DREAMS

The Head Ruler of the Land of Kermit has a chief butler and baker under his command. Many gold dishes of great value have been disappearing, and valuable silverware has also taken flight from the Ruler's household over a period of time. Enraged and incensed at the trespasses and offended by the thefts, he sends them both to prison to give himself time to investigate and determine from where the breach of trust is originating. He places them in custody, under the prison warden, in the proximity of Increase.

They both have vivid dreams and are frightened by them. They are depressed and cower in a prison corner. Increase asks them why they are so scared. The butler tells him he had a dream and doesn't understand it. Increase tells him that UF gives him power to interpret dreams. The butler finally gets the nerve to share his dream with Increase. "I saw a vine before me, and on the vine were three branches. Then blossoms burst forth, and ripe grapes followed. I had my Ruler's cup in my hand and squeezed the grapes into his cup. Then I awoke shivering." Increase is given wisdom from above and interprets the butler's dream. "The three vines are three days. Within three days your status will be restored by your Ruler, and you will once again hand him his drinking cup as you did before. Remember me when you are back in the palace," Increase almost pleads. Now, when the baker hears this great interpretation, he wants Increase to interpret his dream, but Increase doesn't have a good feeling about this one and tries to change the subject. But the baker insists on sharing his dream for the purpose of interpretation. "I dreamt I had three cake baskets on my head. In the top basket were all manner of baked goods for my Ruler. But birds of prey were eating out of the bottom basket that sat on the hair of my head." Increase finds it extremely difficult to share his interpretation, but after the baker's relentless pressing for an answer and hardly able to look him in the eyes, Increase begins: "The three baskets are three days. In three days you will be at a feast hosted by your Ruler with the butler and all his other servants present. All the things you have stolen have been retrieved from your home and brought back to Ruler. The evidence will condemn you to hang, and the birds of prey will eat your flesh." The baker reels back in horror and shakes uncontrollably, in a fetal position. Now the butler understands why he was imprisoned. He had been held under suspicion of theft, theft that the baker had committed.

Just as Increase had said, in three days both the butler and baker are summoned to a feast given by their Ruler. Both their households had been investigated on account of the thefts while they were detained in prison. All the stolen items were found at the baker's home and are repossessed. The butler is found innocent and the baker guilty of stealing all manner of valuables from his Ruler's household. After the banquet he is hanged and left to the birds of prey.

Having been restored, the butler does not remember Increase or his accurate dream interpretations. After two full years, UF gives the Ruler of Kermit a very strong and unusual dream. It is so vivid in color and depth, the Ruler cannot remove it from the forefront of his mind. He is so vexed by it, he searches far and wide for someone to interpret its meaning. He reveals it to any and all in the land who might help him understand what it means, but no one has an answer. Everyone walks away, unable to help him. Finally, the butler remembers Increase and how he was able to interpret his dream and that of the baker and how they came true. He shares this with his Ruler. "There is a young male from the tribe of the Prevailies in prison who works for the warden, who interpreted our dreams accurately," the butler said.

The Ruler summons Increase from prison and asks him if he is able to make sense of the dream. The Voice assures Increase that He will reveal the meaning to him; thus Increase confidently replies, "Yes, I can, by the power of my UF." Ruler relates his dream to him. "I was standing by the banks of the River of Kermit. Coming out of the river were seven beautiful, fat cows chomping at the rich grasses by the bank. Then seven more cows came up out of the river, but these were ugly and emaciated. Then the scary part was that the ugly, skinny cows ate the seven beautiful fat cows. But they remained ugly and skinny, even though they had just devoured the others. After that I awoke. Now tell me, what do you see in this?"

Increase begins speaking. "The seven beautiful, fat cows represent seven years of fruitfulness and plenty in the land. The seven ugly, emaciated cows represent a warning sent by UF of the coming of seven years of famine, hunger, and loss. The seven ugly, emaciated cows eating the seven beautiful, fat cows and still remaining ugly and skinny means that the famine and hunger in the land will be so severe that they will remove any vestige of the plentiful years. Plenty and sufficiency will become totally unknown in this and distant lands. This is UF's message for the Ruler of Kermit."

Increase continues saying, "It is coming very soon upon the Land of Kermit. Ruler should discreetly seek out a wise and proficient one and appoint him governor. He then should appoint officers to report to him for the purpose of taking one-fifth of the produce of the whole Land of Kermit every year during the seven plenteous years. That food should be stored for the nation against the seven years of hunger and famine that are coming. Under the direction and authority of Ruler, grain and food should be stored in granaries within the cities. Then, when the years of famine come, there will be food available so that the Land of Kermit may survive and the people will not die."

THE FULFILLMENT

After Ruler had listened and heard everything Increase had spoken, he thinks it is a very good idea, and he praises him before his other servants. "This son of the Prevailies is unlike any in our land. The spirit of UF is in him, and UF speaks through him! We will listen and be benefited!" He turns to Increase and takes off his signet ring and puts it on him. Next, he gives him royal clothing to change into. When Increase returns, bathed and dressed in his new clothes, Ruler puts a gold chain around his neck. He tells all his household and servants to bow down before him. He tells them that nothing will be done in all the land without first obtaining permission from Increase. He is set above everyone else in the nation, second only to Ruler himself. Ruler then speaks, "His name shall from this day forth be called Revelator!" Ruler also gives Revelator a beautiful, noble daughter of royalty, named Belong, to be his Assistant.

Revelator's life at long last turns for the better. No longer a slave, he can finally enjoy freedom and the comforts attached to his high position. He loves Belong and his new job. He has much responsibility, but with UF's help he is not concerned. He thanks his UF and seeks His Voice constantly. After weeks of resting and refreshing himself with his Assistant, Revelator begins his work.

Just as the Voice had told him and as he had relayed to Ruler, there are seven years of plenty. During those years, Revelator and his Assistant have two sons. He names his firstborn son Forget, because Increase has found new hope and happiness, and his son has caused him to forget his past toils and sorrows. He names his second son Fruitful, because UF has caused him to be fruitful in the land of his affliction. Crops are abundant and rich. No one would ever think that a famine might be on the way. He gathers one-fifth of all the crops of the land for Ruler and his granaries. When the seventh and final year of abundance is fulfilled, the granaries are filled to almost overflowing.

In the eighth year, the rains cease. The crops show signs of weakness. As the ninth and tenth years pass, there are fewer and fewer crops to harvest. By the eleventh and twelfth years, a severe famine is upon the land. Where once lush gardens of food grew, nothing but dust and sand appear. The winds blow and carry away much of the topsoil. Endless numbers of flocks of sheep and herds of cattle die from starvation, as there are no grasses or greens of any kind to be found for hundreds of miles. Many other animals perish from just the lack of water. There is not enough to go around, and what there is must be rationed and conserved.

In the thirteenth and fourteenth years, most of the animal life has perished. They had been the last available food sources used for survivable. Panic begins to set in everywhere. But the Land of Kermit opens its granaries in all its cities and is able to feed its population and keep certain chosen animals alive. The Kermits will not starve. Seeing everything unfold just as Increase had said, Ruler is glad he put him in charge. He is calm and content through this excruciatingly difficult time. All the Kermits have enough food to get them by for many years to come. There is also enough to sell to others who are willing to pay. Revelator sells food to outsiders who come from other near and far lands desperately searching for food and seed sources. He thus helps make the Ruler of Kermit very wealthy. Having completely earned Ruler's trust and the trust of all his Kermits, Revelator is highly respected and held in great esteem throughout the land.

Prevail and his other sons, the brothers of Increase (now Revelator), are running out of their food supplies. Prevail has heard word that the Land of Kermit has plenty of grain and seed available for purchase. He is a wealthy man. But his flocks are getting thin, and they too experience tremendous lack. All the gold and silver he has amassed is now of no use unless he can buy supplies with his wealth. Many deaths have occurred far and wide due to the famine. He has always trusted the Voice and knows that somehow he and his family will get through. He sends all his older sons to the Land of Kermit to buy grain. These are the sons he had with Hefferina. They are also the stepbrothers of Increase, the ones who sold him into slavery, except for Sonsee, who did not want this to happen. He keeps at home with him his youngest son, Rightson, the son of his old age whom he had with Ewenice just before she died in childbirth. Although several of his older sons left home and started families of their own, they have all been brought back together in order to pool their resources and collectively stand against the famine for survival. Prevail gives his sons several sacks of gold and silver to take with them in order to buy and bring back supplies. Then he petitions UF to go before them and bring them back home safely.

Sonsee, Earson, Joiner, Reward, Praise, and Dwell head out on their long journey to the Land of Kermit. Finally reaching their destination, they are sent to a designated checkpoint area where Revelator oversees and approves all non-resident purchases. Having the highest authority in the land, second only to Ruler, Revelator is dressed in fine linens. He wears dark eye makeup, as is customary for all royalty, as well as a special wig and much gold jewelry. He no longer looks like the shepherd boy he once was in his teens. And to everyone in the Land of Kermit, he is known as the Great Revelator.

When his six stepbrothers arrive and take their place in line, Revelator looks up from some of his work and recognizes them. He starts to tremble. Memories flood and overwhelm his mind. He never thought he would ever see any of them again, and after what they did to him, he knew if he ever got the chance to go home they would certainly have killed him. At first, he is not sure how to respond. He remembers the pain they caused him and all they put him through, the years of slavery and imprisonment, the loss of his father and younger brother. He feels nauseated and faint. One of the guards working with him notices his physical distress and asks him if he is all right. Revelator tells him he must get out of the heat of Fun for a few minutes and asks the guard to walk with him. The lines outside will have to wait. They turn into a small building around the corner and drink some cool water as Revelator sits and tries to regain his composure. Seeing that Revelator is fine for the moment, the guard excuses himself and goes back outside to check on the crowds in line. Meanwhile, Revelator spends time with UF and petitions him for help. "Please help me," he pleads. "How shall I deal with them?"

The hungry, weary travelers outside begin to grow impatient waiting in the hot, stagnating lines. Hearing the grumbling, Revelator heads back outside to the scrolls on his desk and the work before him. As his stepbrothers near the front of the line and finally reach his desk, they bow before him on account of his high office. He remembers the dream he had in his youth, where they all bowed before him, including his father. After all these years, the vision has come to pass in a twisted turn of events. It felt strange, all of it: what he had to go through and endure and now this—he has great authority over them. He has the power to do anything he wants with them. He takes a deep breath and tries not to let on who he really is.

Speaking roughly at them, he asks them who they are and why they have come to the Land of Kermit. They answer, "We have come from the Land of Camptown and are Prevailies. We seek to buy bread, grain, and seed. The famine upon our land is very great." Hearing the voices of his stepbrothers and seeing their faces once again brings back the memory of when they threw him into the pit. Like a flood, the pain and the agony of that moment revisit him. He cried for mercy, but they just laughed and callously ate their lunches while he was hurting. Then they sold him into slavery. Revelator decides he is going to have some fun at their expense.

He folds his arms, sits back, and looks at them suspiciously. "So, you say you have come to buy grain and supplies," Revelator states. Unanimously and sheepishly, they respond, "Yes." "I don't believe you," Revelator declares loudly. "I think you are spies who have come to do harm to our land." A collective gasping can be heard, stretching across the line waiting behind them. The crowd grows tenser. Revelator has so much power and authority, no one would dare to cross him. Unnerved, his stepbrothers quickly respond, "We are not spies. We are sons of an honorable orbling, and we have come in peace! Our father is the head of the Prevailies, and he has sent us for food. We have a younger brother at home named Rightson, and we lost another."

"You lost another?" Revelator asks. "Yes," they answer. "He was killed by a wild animal." Now he understands why his father never looked for him; they had told him he had been killed. Revelator's left hand begins to shake from the audacity of the lie he just heard. He tries to hide his hand under his garment so as not to reveal himself.

He fondly remembers his beloved father and younger brother Rightson and momentarily feels a wave of sadness come over him. "And your father?" Revelator asks. "Is he still well?" The brothers again quickly respond, "Yes."

After a fairly long pause, Revelator speaks, "Very well then, if what you say is true, one of you will stay here as my prisoner, while the rest of you go back home to fetch your youngest brother for me as proof. I will give you supplies enough for you and your households until you return. If your younger brother is brought to me, I may believe you and not prosecute all of you as spies. Now leave me!" The guard seizes Earson, the one Revelator points out, and throws him into prison. Revelator remembered all too well how Earson had ruthlessly grabbed him and thrown him into the pit. He also recalled how the loudest laughter came from him and how painfully it had rung in his ears. He had covered them with his hands just to keep from going mad.

Sonsee nearly collapses. He tells his brothers that this has come upon them because of what they had done to Increase many years before. "I told you not to hurt the lad, but you would not listen to me. Now we are indirectly paying for our sins. We are finally reaping what we have sown. This will kill our father. How will he be able to bear the possibility of another loss?" They head home, brooding over what they have to tell their father. When they explain to Prevail what happened in Kermit, Prevail nearly faints. He cannot bear the thought of possibly losing Rightson or having to give him up. After having lost Increase and then Hefferina in years past, he has lovingly clung to his last, favorite son. Rightson made him want to go on and brought him joy. Now that too is at risk and being threatened. He grieves and weeps for quite a spell.

Prevail makes the decision that they will all go together to Kermit.

If there is any chance of his losing Rightson, he feels he must be there to stop it or help in some way. He decides to bring more silver and gold in case he needs to buy freedom for his family. They pack up and head out together, leaving the servants behind to take care of the home front. After several weeks, the six brothers arrive back in Kermit with their father and half-brother in tow. The guards alert Revelator. He has them all brought into one of his personal houses. There is a dining table set up in the large room. Revelator has instructed the guards to seat them at the table in a particular order. When the family is ushered in, they at first do not notice that their seating arrangements are in their birth order. When everyone is finally sitting, including the formerly imprisoned Earson, Revelator has his servants serve the meal and then dismisses all his help and the guards. Alone with his father and brothers, Revelator comes out to greet them. They all quickly bow before him in deference. They look at him, wondering why they are being served a meal. They are famished and the food smells wonderful. Is it to be their last?

Revelator removes his wig. They look at him, not knowing what this means. They still do not recognize him. He begins to weep. Through tears he tells them he is Increase. Prevail walks up to him and looks closely into his eyes for several minutes. "This can't be! He was killed!" He looks at his other sons, completely perplexed. Their eyes look down in avoidance and reveal to him that they have been privy to something he was not. Then he looks back at Revelator. His knees buckle under his weight. Revelator catches him in mid swoon. They give him water, and in a few minutes he is revived. The stepbrothers wish they could run and hide, but there is nowhere to go. Once Prevail has digested this turn of events, he weeps and hugs Revelator. Sonsee and Rightson rush to him and hug him also. The other brothers are afraid to come closer.

They fear they will have hell to pay. After a long while, Revelator calls his other brothers to him and says, "Come, I have forgiven you. What you meant for harm, UF used for good. He sent me ahead so that all of us would be preserved through these precarious years." They hug and weep together for a very long time.

When they are finally ready to eat, their food is cold. But the rare treat of such a sumptuous meal at the height of the famine is more than they could ever have hoped for. Wine is served and relished between bites. The freshly roasted, herbed lamb and wild rice renew their physical strength, and the unexpected reunion, accompanied by forgiveness, renews their hearts. Cold lamb never tasted so good, they all think! As they linger over cups of hot, flavorful tea, they get to enjoy the very rare treat of fresh fruit straight from Ruler's personal stash. This is indeed a good day. They savor the figs, strawberries, and blueberries piled high on sweet cakes, which have not been available to anyone for many, many years.

Revelator introduces his Assistant, Belong, and his two sons to them. They all hug and greet. After spending many days getting reacquainted and renewing his family's strength with good food, he introduces them all to Ruler. Ruler is delighted to meet Revelator's family. He owes his newly acquired wealth and the preservation of his nation to him. He suggests to Revelator that they should come and live in the Land of Kermit. He bequeaths to him and his family a very large area of choice property where they may bring their children and remnant flocks, knowing that the famine years will soon be over because the rains are coming back. He is very fond of Revelator, and knows that UF is definitely with him. He does not want him to leave or join his family and take the favor of UF with him out of the Land of Kermit.

Prevail and his sons go back to Camptown and gather their servants,

Assistants and children. Then they pack up all their belongings and drive the remainder of their flocks to their new home in Kermit. Their brother Revelator is admired and revered throughout the land, and so are all of his children. For many generations, the Kermits honor and love the Prevailies. Many more Prevailies move to the Land of Kermit and are welcomed with open arms. Their successful life styles, which seem to be benefited by UF, rub off on some of the Kermits. Some want to learn to follow the Voice and many do. This pleases UF.

WINDS OF CHANGE

After about 350 orb years, the Prevailies have reproduced and flourished in the land. They now make up almost half of the population. But many Prevailies have lived too well and no longer turn to their UF. They no longer seek His guidance and wisdom and turn to their own ways. Some, instead of changing the Kermits, let the Kermits change them. They participate in wicked ways and offend UF. Only a handful seems to fear Him and choose righteousness. UF shakes His head in disappointment, knowing that they will have to suffer the consequences of their actions. As much as He loves them, He cannot spare them from the choices they make. This is free will at work.

THE DAYS OF DREW

After Revelator had died, and all of his children, and all his brethren, and their children too, many Kermits forgot the accomplishments of Revelator and his people. The People of Prevail had increased mightily in numbers and filled the land of Kermit. For the most part, this was affecting everything in Kermit positively. Traitor does not like any of this. He wants murder and mayhem and strife to abound. There is too much peace and love going on here.

Now there arose a new Ruler over Kermit who does not know Revelator. He does not listen to the Voice, worse yet, he declares himself to be CEO. He has been listening to the whisperings of Traitor and his bunch. He has turned into a control freak, and he reveals his inferiority complex through his paranoid cruelties. He tells his Kermit people, "The Prevailies are more and mightier than we are. Should they decide to join our enemies and fight against us, we will be in grave danger." In his paranoia, he decides to enslave and afflict them. He makes their lives bitter and hard. He also commands the midwives of his country to kill any male babies they might help deliver. But the midwives of Kermit heed the Voice, have compassion on the babies and their mothers, and simply cannot do this nasty deed. As the number of Prevailie births continues to increase, rather than decrease, the Ruler becomes increasingly mad. Becoming one of the first mass baby killers,

144

he orders all male Prevailie newborns to be cast into the river to drown. Anyone not carrying out his orders is subject to death. Many innocent children are put to death. Suddenly there is great agony throughout the land, and the peace that once reigned is instantly gone.

A Prevailie woman named Gloria gives birth to a beautiful son at the time of this madness. She manages to hide him for three months, but when she can no longer safely conceal him, she puts him in a basket, the outside of which she has covered with pitch to make it waterproof and help it float. She lays her beloved child inside the basket, covers him in a cloth, and after desperately petitioning the Voice to save him, she places the basket in the river. She then cries inconsolably. Myrrhwater, the child's older sister, follows the basket as it floats downriver, in the hopes of spying its fate.

Ruler's favorite daughter happens to be in the river bathing when she sees a basket floating by. She has her maids fetch it for her, and when she pulls the cloth back, she finds a healthy, beautiful, crying infant inside. She has always wanted to have and raise a child. Having compassion in her heart for this precious baby, she seizes the opportunity before her and decides to raise him as her own. Assessing that he is most likely a Prevailie child, she purposes to keep this assumption a secret and makes her maids swear not to speak of it. Observing the king's daughter holding, cuddling, and cooing her baby brother, Myrrhwater steps forward to speak to her. She asks the king's daughter if she would like her to find someone to nurse the child for her until he is ready to be weaned. The king's daughter agrees and pays her wages so the child will be properly cared for.

Gloria is thankful to CEO that her son will live, and although he will never know his true mother, her heart is relieved, because she knows he will grow up in a very privileged place. She lovingly finishes nursing him and enjoys the short time she has left before she must forever let go. When Gloria discreetly finishes nursing and weaning her son, his sister brings him back to the king's daughter. The child is now with his adoptive mother, and she is thrilled to have a son of her very own. She names him Drew because she has drawn him out of the water. She is careful never to let her father find out that Drew comes from Prevailie stock. He is an exceptionally handsome child, and she figures no one will ever know.

In the meantime, her father, the Ruler, becomes more aggressive toward the Prevailies. He works them hard, and their lives are bitter. Like any abused captives, they complain unceasingly, not only to their captors but to UF, in their constant petitions for help. Although their sins had landed them in captivity, their cries reach the heart of CEO, and He puts together a plan to deliver them. He also wants to use this opportunity to teach and reach receptive Kermits and other lost orblings.

As Drew reaches adulthood, he increasingly ventures beyond the palace walls. He has grown into a handsome, tall, and strong young male. His mother, the Princess, adores him. He has a presence about him that attracts favor. Even Ruler is taken by him and prefers him to his own son. Ruler's own son is spoiled, disrespectful to his father, and difficult to be around.

Drew begins to see the injustices done to those worked and held in captivity. Unlike the Kermits, he is deeply moved and troubled by the abuses he sees all around him. He sees a Kermit guard beating one of the workers mercilessly, just for the sake of meanness, and he can't stand it. When no one is looking and in righteous anger, he strikes the Kermit who is still beating the Prevailie worker. In his rage over the injustice, his adrenaline is running full bore, and when he strikes there is tremendous force behind the blow. Without realizing it, he has killed the Kermit guard. Scared he will be found out, he buries him in the sand and runs home. However, word reaches the palace from two eyewitnesses who saw the killing. Enraged at the news of Drew's siding with his perceived enemies and killing one of his guards, the Ruler seeks to find him and have him killed. Influenced by Traitor, he is very quick to anger, and unforgiving to boot. His love and appreciation for Drew is instantly vaporized by his raging fury. He is really not right in the head. His foster mother, the Ruler's daughter, hurries to warn the son she has grown to love and helps him so he can flee from her enraged father. She provides him with a horse and enough temporary provisions so he has a chance to get away and hide. Drew runs until he finally ends up a safe distance in the Land of Strife. It is just to the east of the hill country called Rugged. This is the land where the sons of Faithful by his second wife Incense settled and dwelled.

Wells situated outside the towns or villages serve as landmarks and places of meeting. When Drew waters his horse and refills his skins, he witnesses shepherds driving away seven sisters trying to water their animals. He stands up to the shepherds and defends the sisters so that they may water their sheep and horses. The sisters are very grateful and can't help but notice how handsome he is. Not wanting him to get away and hoping to know more about him, they ask him if they could thank him by treating him to a home-cooked meal. He is worn out from his long journey and tired of eating dried meat and nuts, and seven very attractive sisters have just made him an offer he can't refuse. "Yes, thank you. I would love a home-cooked meal," he replies.

The sisters giggle with glee as they lead the kind stranger to their father's house. They show him where he may rest and feed his horse. As is the custom, the gals had done most of the prep work for the meal earlier in the day. They enter the courtyard of the home and close the outside door behind them, and the aroma of roasted meat wafts their way. Hanging over a fiery pit is a succulent and beautifully roasted side of beef. The color is now a perfect, deep brown. Drew's nose is telling him that good stuff is coming. He is really happy and grateful to have been invited. The gals had placed clay drip pans below the meat to catch all the delicious juices. Hanging above the pit is a huge pot of wild rice infused with mushrooms, onions, garlic, and leeks. They had also baked savory flat breads earlier in the day. The seasoned breads are used to dunk into the drippings and help wipe up any residual juices on the clay serving dishes. They take Drew to the water basin just outside the door, and all of them take turns washing their hands. When they step inside the house the sisters introduce Drew to their father. They tell him how Drew helped them at the well and saved them from being driven away by the other shepherds. "Ah, well then, I'm so glad my daughters invited you to dinner. It's the least we can do to repay your kindness," he says. "I am Eminent, the local priest of Strife, and have been blessed with seven beautiful daughters who work very hard. My Assistant died before she could give me any sons. We manage as best we can. Come, let us eat now while the food is ready and hot, and we will continue our talks."

Drew enjoys being with Eminent very much, and the two get along well. Eminent invites Drew to stay with him and his family as long as he likes. Drew agrees, and in return he handles all the heavy work around the home that needs to be done now that Eminent has become too old to do it himself. Eminent and his daughters warmly welcome the reliable, newfound masculine helper.

They all get along nicely and Drew is happy to have found a safe home. After a few years, Drew finds himself falling in love with

Eminent's eldest daughter. She is named Beauty because she is very beautiful. Eminent is aware of the bond taking place between the two, and when the time is right, he happily gives his daughter to Drew to be his Assistant. A year later Beauty bears a son. Drew names him Foreigner, because he is born while Drew is a foreigner in the Land of Strife. Drew takes care of Eminent's flocks of sheep and other animals. He watches over all the sisters and their aging father and helps add a little balance to the all-female household, except for his now newborn son.

Forty years pass, and the Ruler of Kermit is known to have died. His spoiled and bratty son gains control of the land. His father never disciplined him, so he grew up with a huge sense of entitlement. He is callous, self-centered, uncaring and devoid of empathy. He continues the brutality his father launched against the Prevailies. In fact, because of his empty soul, he takes cruelty to new heights. UF hears the cries of His selected people, the ones through whom He has been able to perpetuate His Voice and ways. Through the lineage of Ally (renamed Faithful), Promise, and Grasp (renamed Prevail), UF finds a cultivat-able remnant with open hearts who seek after Him. Whenever they seek Him and follow His will, they remove Traitor's authority over their lives. Long suffering and ever hopeful, UF works unceasingly to woo any through His Voice who will heed it to come under His authoritative protection. He has a Master Plan in mind to save his selected orblings from the wrath of the Kermit Ruler, who is clearly under the influence and authority of Traitor. Having cultivated His selected line, He is now able to do more works through them, which in turn will be a further witness to other orblings.

One day while Drew is tending to his father-in-law's sheep up in the hills, CEO decides to pay him a personal visit. Drew hears a loud voice address him. He looks around but sees no one. Then he hears the loud voice address him again. He knows the voice is not of this orb, and the thunderous sound brings him to his knees. On his knees, he almost feels paralyzed as the power field of CEO surrounds him. CEO then speaks to Drew. *"I want you to go back to Kermit and tell Ruler to let my people go. I will help you lead them out of Kermit into the land I have promised your forefathers—the promised land of Prevail."*

After hearing this, Drew begins to argue with his UF. He does not want to face his stepbrother. Before he had killed the guard, Drew was Ruler's favorite, even above his own son. His stepbrother was such a rotten character, his father did not like him very much, and everyone in the palace thought Drew would ultimately inherit authority over the land. Now that the brat is in charge, Drew just assumes that his life will be toast if he ever shows his face again. "But, Father," he implores, "I am not a good speaker. My communication skills are limited at best." CEO's Voice booms back, *"I will speak through you!"* Again, Drew argues, "If I go back they will kill me. My stepbrother hates me." CEO assures him, *"I will be with you, and no one will lay a hand on you."* Again Drew tries to argue his way out of the job. CEO is now getting agitated with his reluctance. *"Can I not use an ass if I choose? Therefore, do not irritate me any further. Go and do as I say so that your people may be set free. I will be with you every step of the way."* CEO now leaves. Shaken and numb from the exchange, Drew finally picks himself up and slowly begins to walk again. He brings the sheep back to the vicinity of his father-in-law's house and tells the family what has happened.

With his Assistant and son, they pack up and start on the journey that CEO has assigned to him. They head toward the Land of Kermit, and the Voice gives him instructions on what to do before he meets with Ruler. Upon arrival, Drew meets with all the elders of the Prevailies. He informs them that UF has heard their cries and is about to deliver them out of bondage. They are to prepare for the exodus. Then Drew walks right into the palace where Ruler is arrogantly sitting in his chair. He walks down the long aisle, walks right up to Ruler, and says to him, "The Voice has spoken: *Let the Prevailies go!*" Ruler is stunned that anyone would dare speak to him that way. After all, everything is under his thumb. When the expression of his shock wears off his countenance, he begins to laugh. All his subjects, not knowing what to do, begin to laugh with him. Soon the entire palace chamber is echoing with the sounds of snickering and laughter. Drew just stands there, unruffled. When the laughter dies down, he once again speaks. "The Voice of the UF has spoken: *Let the Prevailies go!*" Now Ruler begins to get angry. How dare anyone tell him what to do! His obstinacy raises its ugly head. And with that he smirks at his stepbrother and gloats as he says, "Never!"

CEO is with Drew and instructs him on what to say next. "I did not come here of my own free will. The UF sent me, and it is His will that the Prevailies be set free. He has told me it will not go well with you if you do not follow His instructions." Ruler sits back in his chair, takes a deep breath and says, "I do not believe in your UF, nor fear him. Now go and leave me before I kill you." Drew says, "Very well, I will leave, but UF will strike the Land of Kermit with His power, after which you will let His people go!"

CEO is angry! What nerve this twit of a Ruler has! He turns all the water in Kermit into transmission fluid. The stench fills the land, and no one is able to drink. But Ruler stubbornly refuses to let the Prevailies go. Now CEO begins to play a game with him. He releases millions of frogs to freak out all the inhabitants. You would think that by now Ruler would think something is clearly up. But again, he hunkers down in his stubbornness and refuses to let the Prevailies go. CEO shakes his head and rains down millions of Traitor's specially-mutated lice upon them. Again, Ruler, who seems brain dead, will not budge from his position. Really fed up with Ruler's audacity, CEO unleashes more of his righteous fury. He sends pestilence, boils, hail, locusts, and darkness. The people of Kermit are terrified to say the least, but the arrogant Ruler will still not acquiesce.

Having his fill of fun and games, CEO sends an Agent of death to all the firstborn in every Kermit family, including that of Ruler's household. CEO spares the Prevailie firstborns. Before unleashing his final fury, He instructs Drew to deliver the warning message of what is to come upon them, in the hopes that Ruler will listen before He has to follow through on His threat. But the idiot Ruler neither believes in UF, nor His power, nor that anyone can effect such a decree. And thus, CEO activates the Agent of death to carry out His final persuasive tactic. Within two days, the entire Land of Kermit is brought to its knees. There is weeping and gnashing of teeth. Even Ruler's firstborn has been struck down. As death finishes passing across the Land, the stubborn, beaten dictator finally succumbs to Drew's edicts and the will of UF.

The Prevailies pack up, and UF tells them to ask the Kermits for whatever they need or want on their journey. He is about to lead them to a land of their very own. A land promised to them by UF that He says is a land of milk and honey. The Kermits are now completely frightened of the Prevailies and give them gold, clothing, animals, food supplies, and anything else they desire. Drew leads them out of Kermit bondage and takes them through the desert in the direction CEO instructs. When they reach the Crimson Sea, they must stop and rest for a while.

Back at the palace, Ruler's anger has reached a fever pitch. He has a change of mind and is mad that he let the Prevailies go. Always getting his way, he can't believe this has happened to him. Because Traitor has whispered in his ear since he was a young boy and Ruler has always chosen to listen to him, his mind has been irreversibly corrupted. In his total madness, he decides to head up his army of warriors and go after the Prevailies to kill every last one of them. They are, after all, unarmed and with children out in the desert. Finishing them off should be easy, and he thinks it would sure be sweet revenge if he could slaughter all of them. He is so incensed at being defeated, he can no longer see straight.

UF sees his heart and knows what is coming. He hoped that the fool would fear Him and let the Prevailies go on their way, but this is not to be. The Prevailies, resting in front of the sea, look up because they hear a thunderous sound coming their way. Thousands of Ruler's horses and chariots filled with armed soldiers kick up the sand as they speed through the desert canyon heading straight for Drew and all the freed Prevailies. Panic sets in among them because they realize they are completely boxed in. Their eyes widen as they see the approaching menace, and many let out screams of despair.

UF tells Drew to stand on a stone outcropping by the sea and raise his walking stick and then speak His words to the terrified crowds. Drew lifts his walking stick and shouts out, "Behold the mighty hand of UF!" Suddenly the Crimson Sea begins to part right before their very eyes. Drew tells them to hurry through the passage before the soldiers reach them. Hundreds of thousands begin to run for their lives into the scary, narrow channel. The sea wall is high all around them, held back by two invisible walls. If they hadn't been facing the chariots from hell coming at them, they would not have been brave enough to face the walls of water. They run through as fast as their feet will take them, terrified not just by the oncoming army, but also by the massive, suspended sea walls above and around them, held back by a strange and invisible force.

It is amazing how many hundreds of thousands manage to cross to the other side within a fairly short period of time. Ruler and his army observe the great escape and can't believe their eyes. Then he commands the army to follow and destroy them. The Prevailies look back and begin to scream again as they see the Kermit army simply follow after them through the channel. As the last Prevailies, with all their booty, make it to the other side, the Kermit army is three-quarters of the way to reaching them. But before they reach the other side, the invisible walls that held back the sea melt away, and the waters fall back in on themselves, devouring every last soldier in hot pursuit of the selected people.

When the violent event is at last over and the sea has returned to its normal boundaries, the shaken Prevailies look back. They fall to their knees from the sheer terror of it all and remain traumatized for several days simply trying to process and digest what they have just survived. It takes several more days until their state of shock finally dissipates and they once again are able to move forward.

Drew leads his people onward, under the direction of UF. They are three days away from reaching the Land Promised. Completing their first full day of travel, they settle in for the night. By the third day, they have arrived in the wilderness called Enclosure. UF has led them there to test their faith in Him. The waters there are bitter and undrinkable. They murmur and complain, rather than petitioning their UF. He watches from above, shaking His head at their complete unbelief. He has just parted the Crimson Sea for them. They feel hopeless again and think He has left them to die. He instructs Drew to perform another miracle for these stiffed-necked people. He imbues a fallen tree with just the right chemicals and life-giving properties and tells Drew to get several strong helpers and throw it into the water. When the tree infuses the bitter water with its properties, the water becomes potable. He reveals another mystery of the Tree of Life, but none of them see nor decipher the clue He has them drop into the water—a tree to bring forth life where there once was death. Once again UF shows His selected people that He will be with them. He tells Drew that He will take care of their every need if they will honor Him and His boundaries.

USER'S MANUAL

After three months in the wilderness, before dawn one morning, Drew is drawn by the Voice to head into the hills. UF wants to personally meet with him. Drew leaves his people and tells them to honor UF's boundaries and that he will return when he is dismissed by the Voice. Drew begins his ascension up a mountain known as Mount Truth. When he is near the top, UF visits with him. The mountain quakes as UF sets foot upon it. Drew is terrified. His knees are shaking, and his face reveals a sobering encounter with a serious force. But his faith in UF keeps him upright and moving forward. This is also why he was chosen. The Voice speaks. Lightening bolts and thunder strike all around Drew, but miss him. *"Today I Am giving you a condensed version of the User's Manual for My Heirs."* The Voice continues to boom throughout the mountain canyons. *"These are My instructions:*

No. 1: You must not put any other CEO before Me.

No. 2: You must not make anything else your CEO, nor worship them in My stead.

No. 3: You must not take the name of your CEO in vain.

No. 4: You must remember the day of R&R and honor it.

No. 5: You must respect your mother and father so that your days may be long.

No. 6: You must not murder.

No. 7: You must not commit adultery.

No. 8: You must not steal.

No. 9: You must not lie or bear false witness.

No. 10: You must not long with envy for anything that is not yours."

As the Voice finishes booming the instructions, a shale outcropping is simultaneously engraved with a precision laser- light cutter ensconced within the lightning bolts. When the writing is complete, the shale splits off into two thin tablets. The Voice tells Drew to pick them up and says:

These two tablets are an abbreviated version of My User's Manual for you—My Heirs. You must tell the people to follow the instructions written thereon. Successful living and overcoming are found within these boundaries. Those who transgress my instructions will find death and destruction. I have written My orders in stone for you as a symbol of the certainty of My universal laws. In other words, everything within the Universe is set up to respond to My fixed regulations. Just as surely as night follows day, spring follows winter, and My gravitas keeps everything in its place, so do my boundaries. Therefore, read and follow them so that all will go well with you and yours. Now take these and return to your people. Many are already incurring my wrath with their actions since your absence.

Drew begins his descent and return. Approaching the camp, he finds some of them dancing around a huge bonfire and worshiping all the gold they had collected from the Kermits prior to their departure. Some are engaged in orgies and other lewd conduct. Instead of being grateful to UF for having unshackled and saved them from the Kermits' abuses, they are pricking CEO's ire by worshiping their newly-acquired possessions and committing all sorts of immoral acts. CEO is incredibly angry. This was to be His selected people, a pedigree from which He was cultivating a lifeline to save the Heirs. And now they too are turning to debauchery. He speaks to Drew and says, *"I will make a great nation out of you and your descendents and will destroy all these others. I have had it with this lot of stiff-necked people. I brought them out of bondage, sent plagues to their enemies, parted the sea for them, and this is the thanks I get!"*

Drew is frightened for his friends and the people he has grown to care for. Having the faith to believe UF's Voice, Drew speaks it back to Him and petitions Him to keep His original Word. He petitions UF for mercy. "Please do not destroy the successions of Faithful, Promise, and Prevail. You Yourself have said and sworn that they will inherit the Land Promised. You cannot lie. Therefore please do not destroy them." CEO is taken aback by Drew's boldness and faith in holding UF to His previously spoken Voice. He is impressed with this Prevailie because he seems to understand the ordinances of UF. *"Well spoken, Drew. My Voice shall stand, just as you said."* Finally, CEO thinks to Himself, *an orbling of substance!* And thus, the Master Architect backs down from His threat and desire to destroy the entire lot of Prevailies.

Drew gathers his people before him and says, "Those of you who will honor UF stand by me, and those who choose to defy His Voice stand over there." About 3,000 defiantly move to the other side. They do not want to honor UF or live by His instructions. Drew calls his people to slay them. Because of their disobedience, all could have perished. After explaining to everyone what UF was about to do, they all feel it is better that these rebellious ones be killed, rather than have the ire of UF come against the rest of them and have all perish on their account.

Drew goes back to Mount Truth to once again meet with UF. He asks forgiveness for the rebellion of his people and tells UF that, if necessary, he will take the sins of the people upon himself. "Kill me if you must, but please spare my people." UF speaks to Drew and says, *"I will punish those who rebel against Me, not you. Now go and lead your people to the place I have prepared for you. One of My Secret Agents will lead the way. I will drive out your enemies in the land promised to you. But I will not engage in fellowship among your stiff-necked people, lest I grow angry again and destroy them."*

By the time Drew returned to his people, many had perished from a plague. These were the ones who came against UF but did not reveal themselves when Drew had called them out. The unbelief and continuous sinning of thousands of Prevailies keep angering UF. The last straw takes place when the Secret Agent leads them right to the Land Promised, and the Prevailies are afraid to go in and take possession. They do not trust UF. They bicker among themselves. Although three try to convince the rest that they need to take possession of the Land, just as UF has told them to, they are outnumbered by the naysayers. Totally fed up with them, UF leaves them to their foolish fears. They wander in circles through the wilderness, and what should have been a three-day journey has now turned into 40 years. UF is so disgusted with them that He decides that no Prevailie over the age of 20 shall enter the Land Promised. He proclaims to them that all the older, unbelieving, sinful generation must die off first. The leadership of the Prevailies is formally transferred to Deliverer, a close aide of Drew.

When Drew is 120 years old, UF leads him to the high hills surrounding the Land Promised called "the Hills of His Father." Upon reaching the top of Mount Prophecy, Drew can clearly see the land before him. Even in his old age, his eyesight is still excellent. It is beautiful, and he is thankful that UF allows him to experience the sight of it. He weeps tears of joy and tears of pain. He knows he will not enter, but he is comforted to know that finally the younger successions of Prevailies will, at long last, come into their Land Promised.

Drew and UF share sweet fellowship for a very long while, and then he dies. CEO charges His Agent, Little CEO, to contend with Traitor. Traitor knows this Heir was and will be used mightily by his CEO. He wants to completely decimate his physical remnant, because he knows that CEO has plans to once again raise him in the last days as a powerful witnessing tool. Little CEO contends mightily to fight off Traitor and, by the power of the Voice, wins. For the first time in Favored's history, CEO personally buries the body of Drew in these hills. He does this so that neither orbling nor Castaway can discover where the body lies.

CEO allows the Prevailies 30 days to mourn the loss of Drew. At the end of that time period, He calls upon Deliverer to assume command over the Prevailies and lead them into the Land Promised. *"I will be with you, I will help you fight your enemies, and I will establish you in this Land. Now gather your people and take the Land. It shall be called Prevail,"* CEO says. With the help of their UF and the Commander Deliverer they enter the Land of Prevail. The Prevailies live in this land continuously from the time of its original settlement by Deliverer, even though they are not always in control or in the majority.

SPREADING THE VOICE

Generations of Prevailies spread the Voice and honor UF. Through the centuries, previous successions and future ones document their history. UF-inspired manuscripts begin to emerge and are passed down to future generations. Just like a well-written book, precepts, facts, and stories come together until a complete set of scrolls form. Through these ultimate writings, the Heirs are able to learn about their roots. From life stories and examples depicted within the scrolls, they glean insights into the love of CEO, the purpose for their lives, and how to live successfully. Throughout the generations, the Voice has announced that UF will send a Restorer who will save His orblings. The faithful, selected ones have been teaching their children of the coming Restorer, who will deliver them from the grip of Traitor and his death spiral.

They learn of Headquarters and the Land of the Fired. Word filters down that the Land of the Fired is a place of exile, a place intended only for Traitor and his Castaways. But because of his deceptions and the Heir's evil choices, many are being dragged along. Completely void of the CIA, there is nothing but torment. The CIA is the only source of warmth and life. Outside the watchful eye of the CIA lie emptiness, darkness, and death. Just like branches cut from the tree, there is no life apart from UF and His CIA at Nucle-Eye. But Traitor keeps telling the Heirs there is no Land of the Fired and there is no Headquarters.

Having authority over the orb, he works hard to convince them that their life on Favored is all there is, that there is no day of reckoning, and that they should live it up while they can.

However, the influence of the Voice-heeding Prevailies is making a positive mark on Favored and its inhabitants. The Voice is being written and preserved for future generations. The respect of UF is being taught and passed on. Many Heirs seek and long to reconnect to their UF. They understand the destruction and pain that Traitor has brought upon them. They try hard to follow UF's instructions; however, even the best of them usually still fail from time to time. Now they cling to the hope of the promised Restorer; the One who will make them whole again and show them the way back to their inheritance at Headquarters.

CREATION OF THE FBI

Traitor's conniving had tricked Atom and E.V. into transgressing CEO's boundary, thereby mutating their DNA before they were able to replicate. Simply put, DNA is the code of life on a molecular level that holds all hereditary information passed from one generation to another—the stuff that caused Atom and E.V. to look like the CIA and act like them. CEO told them that His life is in the transmission fluid He passed on to them.

However, at the Transgression/Mutation, the war within them manifested outside of them, and the perfect line was broken. In the nucleus of each transmission fluid cell are chromosomes, the rod-like, structured vehicles of genetics. The genes that were once whole and healthy, thereby able to connect with similar genes to appear in the next generation of producing cells, were mutated. Now two mutated genes from each parent will continue to produce this line of now-dominant genes. The transmission fluid does more than just supply physical life. The fluid makes atonement for CEO's life endowment. All fragmentation in the endowment comes from the battle that has entered into the DNA. If Traitor knows there is something within the Heirs that is not in alignment with CEO's way of thinking, he will take that resource under his control. His ultimate goal is to vex the spirit (life endowment) of the Heirs so that CEO's life force cannot be released to them. All wars on the orb are connected on one level or another to the spilling of transmission fluid which is why all wars cause transmission fluid shedding.

After eons of joyful imagineering, creationism must take a backseat to repair and maintenance. The CIA turns Its attention toward saving and restoring its Heirs. Legal authority of their lives and the orb must be returned to CIA stewardship. The remaining loyal Agents, who have proved their devotion, watch as CEO and His BT brainstorm over how to legally take back the treehouse and the beloved children in it.

They begin by establishing the Office of Forgiveness Based Immunization (FBI). Multiple legions of Agents are assigned to report to the FBI for investigative and undercover work. Discretion will be required in order to properly protect and launch this delicate operation. Behind closed doors at FBI offices, CEO and His BT are underwriting the very first Universal "endowment insurance policy." The birth of this endowment will launch the AVP (All-Mighty Virus Protection) and apply all actions. The AVP will be offered and freely given to anyone who accepts this gift of immunization and believes in its restorative powers.

Although a small remnant is somewhat healthy, due to the fact that they heed the Voice and thereby avoid further damage, all orblings have damaged hard drives because the offspring of Atom and E.V. have passed on mutated DNA. Those who have stopped heeding the Voice are degenerating at an even more rapid pace.

After the Transgression/Mutation there is no pure source of transmission fluid available among the successions of Atom and E.V. that can be used as an anti-viral antidote. The loyal Agents' transmission fluid, though similar to the Heirs', contains enough differing numbers of chromosomal pairs to totally void a match. The animals also have differing chromosomal makeups. Knowing this fact because of the eons he had spent at Nucle-Eye Headquarters, Traitor smugly thinks he has outsmarted and defeated CEO's plans. As far as he knows, there are absolutely zero suitable donors available from whom an anti-viral antidote can be made.

BIRTHING THE AVP ENDOWMENT

When the endowment underwriting is completed, the FBI plans for birthing the first cosmic AVP start to materialize. City Headquarter's brainstorming is in full swing. The giant screen comes alive with multiple images of the Tree of Life superimposed over the bold, crimson cross. At the intersection sits Favored and the beloved Heirs. Everything CEO and His Brain Trust have created and love now lies directly in the crosshairs of fate. CIA's three major creations (the Agents, the Universe, and the Heirs) are now fully engaged in a cathartic sifting that will once again separate darkness from light. Proposals are drafted on various ways to redeem the race of orblings from the sickness and deception that occurred at the Transgression/Mutation. After much trepidation, it becomes clear there is only one way. Aware that nothing good ever comes easy, the CIA unanimously decides to embark on a dangerous covert operation. Little CEO, Strong Man, and a handful of their officers are entrusted with the details of this highly sensitive mission. Fully aware of the magnitude of this endeavor and totally trustworthy, they act with the utmost discretion.

Having passed His pure, consecrated transmission fluid to His Heirs at their creation, CEO is the only perfect donor match. He must personally return to Favored, re-establish intimacy, and activate the AVP. If He returns to Favored in His full power, the negative bandwidths on the orb will compel Him to kill the orblings on sight. He also knows that if He comes as the powerful CEO, the Heirs will not be able to relate to Him and thus He will not be able to reconcile many. He is always foremost after re-establishing intimacy and relationship. He wants to be in a more sympathetic state so He can slowly inoculate by invitation and word-of-mouth testimonies. He makes a gut-wrenching but necessary executive decision. With the backing, love, and guidance of the BT, He decides to incarnate an aspect of Himself in order to create a second Atom, and a pure transmission fluid source.

The CIA knows that the transmission fluid of a baby orbling does not pass through or mix with the fluid of the mother in her womb. Therefore, by inseminating a virgin womb, His incarnated aspect will safely be born without any danger of His transmission fluid being mixed or defiled. Because the Heirs were created in His own image, He will be comfortable in their skin. He will glean additional first-hand experiences of their weaknesses and better understand and sympathize with what they are going through. He will also be able to relate to His Heirs on their level, while at the same time restraining and camouflaging the magnitude of His full power and supernatural greatness, so that they will not be blown away by His presence.

In countless meetings with the BT and His most trusted Secret Agents, preparations are readied for His journey into the physical realm. The great CEO's aspect will be the first "time traveler" of sorts in the Universe. Because of His great love, He allows Himself to be birthed into a physical, time- and space-restricted dimension. The BT makes arrangements for the special protection of CEO's aspect while in the delicate baby stage and childhood years.

They search hearts for a tender loving, suitable special Assistant who heeds and seeks the Voice, one who will nurture and tenderly love her infant so that He will grow emotionally healthy and physically strong. The orbly father must also be very special, one who will heed the Voice and accept the responsibility of being the protector of both the impregnated Assistant and child.

Strategizing continues as risks are assessed. Traitor and his Castaways must continue to think they have won the battle and be clueless regarding the sacrifice that CEO is about to make, as well as the details of how it will be carried out. Millions of covert FBI Agents will be unleashed upon the orb just before, during, and after the delicate operation.

Once again, the actions of the CIA reveal some of Its mysteries. It always seems to be curiously involved in productions and phases of three. As the pregnancy plans of the CIA become known, Headquarters begins Its birth pangs. The CIA willingly releases an aspect of CEO. When the chromosomal DNA taken from Him is artificially inseminated into the chosen vessel, His only-begotten aspect will begin to grow. At inception, He will be split off from CEO and become the first-born, Wholly Son of the CIA and will possess pure, un-mutated DNA. This now will create the third aspect within the CIA, i.e., the CEO, The Son, and The BT. Because the Son will be the second Atom, He takes the second position within the Tri-Unity. As always, everything the CIA produces has a mind-blowing mathematical base. One plus one makes two. The two is the third aspect, and the first born of the equation.

THE SEARCH FOR FOSTER PARENTS

After thorough investigative procedures have been launched and satisfied, the worthy Heiress is located. A young female, named Bittersweet, always seeking the Voice and petitioning for His will and counsel is located. Her loyalty brings the CIA great joy. Her fiancé is called Augment, and he is also an ardent Voice seeker. The two are making plans to become one, getting to know each other better, and honoring the customary waiting period prior to their ceremonial union. One afternoon, while Bittersweet is walking by herself, seeking the Voice's guidance, as she usually does, Agent Strong Man greets her. He shows her his FBI credentials and tells her he has been sent by the FBI to speak with her. He tells her that she is going to give birth to the long awaited and promised Restorer. This son of CEO will be the AVP for the race of orblings.

Bittersweet asks Strong Man how this can be, since she is still a virgin. Agent Strong Man replies that she will be anesthetized before the BT comes upon her and artificially inseminates her with CEO's aspect. She replies, "According to the Voice, let it be done to me." A few hours later, Bittersweet wakes up from sleeping and finds she is alone. Not quite sure what has happened or if she was just dreaming, she hurries home. After missing two menstrual cycles, she realizes that her encounter with the FBI Agent was real. Although overwhelmed with excitement at having been chosen as the one to carry the promised Restorer, reality now sets in on what might happen to her once her pregnancy begins to show. She is not yet officially united to Augment, and the customs of her day demand that a pregnant, ununited female receives a rock party. In the name of UF, they stone the poor gal to death. Although CEO always wants His orblings to live uprightly, that they may have a better life, Traitor has convinced the males to deal treacherously with the females who stumble, while managing to once again lay the blame on CEO.

After five months, Augment realizes that Bittersweet is pregnant, and because he has waited for her, he knows he is not the father. She tells him what happened to her when she met the FBI Agent on her walk. He listens but finds her story farfetched. Speechless, he leaves her. Deeply wounded and numb from the discovery and her unbelievable tale, he is shocked and feels utterly betrayed. He thought he knew her better. He spends the next few days alone in the hills with a broken heart, trying to make sense of what has happened. Augment is no longer excited and doesn't want to take her as his Assistant. But he is a kind orbling and has no desire to see Bittersweet hurt or killed, so he ponders how he can arrange for her to be sent away quietly so that no one will know of her transgression. He also spends many hours petitioning the Voice and asking for help on how to best handle this sticky situation.

Late one evening, while he is sleeping, he receives instruction in a most vivid and unmistakable dream. He is told not to send Bittersweet away. Just as she has said, she is pregnant with the Son of CEO. He is told not to be afraid to take Bittersweet as his Assistant. She *is* carrying the long-awaited, promised Restorer. When he awakes, Augment is once again left speechless, but this time for a different reason. He now begins to get it: the honor and the seriousness that have been thrust upon him and Bittersweet. They have been entrusted with a tremendous gift and responsibility.

The next morning, he spends an hour in the counsel of the Voice, after which his heart is completely healed from the perceived betrayal. His heart once again filled with love, he departs for Bittersweet's home. Having gone through some anxious days and still unsure how her relationship with Augment will end, Bittersweet is outside, hanging clothes on a line. From a distance, she sees the figure of an orbling approaching her house that looks like it might be him. Her heart leaps in hope. As the figure draws nearer, she sees that it is Augment. He keeps walking until he walks right into her arms and holds her ever so tightly. Without either speaking a word, both know they are meant to be together.

Four months later, while they were traveling through the City of Bread, Augment is earnestly looking for a room where he and Bittersweet may lodge for the night and come in out of the cold. She is very close to giving birth. But every room in town is taken, and no one takes pity on her condition or predicament. In desperation, Augment manages to find an enclosed barn that provides a roof and shelter from the wind and cold. With the barn door closed, they make a bed in the hay by covering it with the skins and fur blankets they had packed. Together they snuggle to keep warm as the darkness of night creeps over the landscape. That evening, Bittersweet begins having contractions. The Son of CEO, the long-awaited Restorer and AVP, is about to be released into the physical realm for the purpose of providing an antidote and technical support to His beloved Heirs. They are sick and lost, and in desperate need of healing and direction. As beads of perspiration appear upon Bittersweet's forehead and the pain intensifies with increasingly-frequent contractions, she hears the Voice declare in a very loud audible manner, *"This child you deliver tonight will deliver you!"*

After CEO's aspect is born, they wrap him in a blanket. Bittersweet holds him close to her heart and kisses him. Augment lovingly puts his arms around both of them, as tears of joy stream down his face. They smile at each other and take turns holding their "little miracle." Suddenly, from out of nowhere, the barn door flies open and the sound of fluttering wings fills the air. Once inside the barn, with the door closed again, bright lights reveal Agents dropping to their knees before the baby, crying, "Wholly, Wholly, is the son of CEO. He will be called Ransom." And so Bittersweet and Augment name their newborn Ransom, just as the Agents have said. The following morning three wise priests sent by the FBI find the newborn and his parents in the barn. Knowing that this child is the Restorer, they bestow the young parents with valuable gifts and gold to ensure that all their needs will be met.

THE FIRST COOKIE

In His formative years, Ransom is loved, comforted, and protected by his wonderful orbling parents. They have settled in the Town of Branch, nearby which passes the main road of traffic between Kermit and the interior of the East Land. Augment moved his family there because of the availability of work in a neighboring city seven miles away. Much growth and building is taking place, and many products are sought after. Ransom now also has several other siblings. Legions of Secret Agents are assigned to keep constant watch over Him and His family. He is guided by a powerful force that draws Him daily. Even when He is very young, He spends many hours alone in order to commune with CEO and the BT. The BT lovingly hovers over Him and gifts him with His first chocolate chip cookie. He tastes the cookie and finds it incredibly sweet and delicious, and He receives rest and renewal from the encounter. Receiving unorbly guidance and wisdom from above, He is already light years ahead in maturity for His age before He is a teenager. Not long after, He realizes that He is not of this orb, nor of this family, but rather from above.

In His late teens, He finds and develops a trade. Inexplicably drawn to trees, He naturally gravitates to working with wood. He clearly has a thing for trees and enjoys creating and building furniture and various objects out of the indigenous woods available. He designs and makes some of the finest furniture that the locals have ever seen. He loves to build things with His hands and to teach and counsel, as well as offer technical support to anyone who asks for help. He finds a perfect tree in town, in which He builds a treehouse for the children. After many months of work, it is finally finished. It is big enough to accommodate ten to twelve children at a time, yet is still wondrously charming. The youngsters are thrilled, and it quickly becomes their favorite local hang-out. Ransom's loving gesture buys Him the attention and ears of many admiring children. He uses this advantage to teach and guide them in the ways of the Voice. Children bring Him much pleasure and hope, and He spends a great deal of time with them, showing them what real love is supposed to look like.

THE SECOND COOKIE

By about the age of 30, Ransom has honed His skill of teaching. In another one of His solitary moments with CEO and the BT, He is given His second chocolate chip cookie. Uploading the chips in this cookie removes the amnesia given to Him at birth, and completely restores His physical body to His spiritual essence. While He was growing up as an orbling and prior to His complete physical maturation, His psyche was being protected from knowing everything about His birth. Now that His appointed time has come, His true parents reveal Themselves to Him and tell Him that His orbling parents are actually His foster parents. He quickly understands who He is and why He agreed to participate in this incarnation. He has long suspected that He was not of this orb. Now He has a new, laser-like focus about the work that must be done. The cookie has also enabled and released the true powers within Him.

Filled with fresh revelations about His mission and with His powers enabled, He sets out to bring restoration through the spreading of the good news of the availability of the AVP. By choosing to be inoculated with the AVP, orblings will be able to unshackle themselves in two ways. One, if they choose, they will have renewed intimacy with their UF, and two, they will also have the ability to deny Traitor authority over their lives and give it back to UF, the One who really loves them and has their best interests at heart. He also teaches them that petitioning their UF is the ultimate wireless connection.

Now that the Son of CEO has reached full maturity in the flesh and is unleashed spiritually, Traitor and his Castaways immediately recognize Him. Like a powerful beam of light in a pitch-black room, His presence is unmistakable. They are pissed! Traitor is clearly unnerved. For 4,000 orb years (which to them was the blink of an eye) they have wreaked havoc upon the orb and destroyed many Heirs. They did not want the party to end. A million thoughts and questions cross Traitor's mutinous mind. *What is He doing in my domain?* he ponders. *I thought He had given up and resigned Himself to the fact that they chose my authority. What is He doing in the physical realm? He looks just like His Heirs! What is this?*

Seeking after the BT, Ransom ends up in a barren region. He finds Himself far from any food source and feels extremely tired and famished. Traitor has been secretively following Him and is happy to find Him in such a precarious position. He is curiously amused and, at the same time, amazed at the logic behind the Son of CEO ensnaring Himself in physical matter, with all its restrictions. Feeling smug and less threatened due to Ransom's weakened condition and physical limitations, he decides to approach Him.

Besides being exhausted and hungry, Ransom finds Himself exposed to a familiar stench. He is able to smell the approaching menace. Traitor relishes the thought of taunting any aspect of his former Boss. "If you really are the Son of CEO, you should have no problem turning this hot sand into buttered popcorn for yourself," he says smugly. But Ransom remains silent and looks down at the sand. Traitor mocks Him, saying, "If you really are the Son of CEO, why don't you just fly back to town? Even I can do that!" Again Ransom is silent.

Feeling ever smugger, Traitor now says, with a growing smirk on his face, "If you will serve me, I will give you food and control over this whole orb!" Ransom slowly raises His head, meets Traitor's haughty gaze, and declares, *"When I get around to serving you, it will be at your sentencing!"* The growing smirk quickly dissolves. In an instant, Traitor begins to perspire profusely and then starts to shake. As he did in the Great Ruby Hall at Headquarters when he faced CEO, he reels backwards, turns on his heels, and splits the scene in a flash. Within minutes, the BT hovers over Ransom, ministers to His needs, and guides Him safely back to town.

THE PLOT SICKENS

Visibly shaken from his encounter with Ransom and frustrated by its outcome, Traitor elevates his hatred and scheming. With a renewed fever pitch, he purposes to bring about the destruction of Ransom. Fiendishly possessed with unbelievable anger, he shudders and loses his cool at the very mention of Ransom's name. He has allowed himself to be totally consumed by his hatred. Thus, the very first possessed being on Favored is Traitor, the Atom Smasher Specialist himself, or, as CEO's loyal Agents love to call him, A.S.S. for short. As he roams the orb, he will seek orblings who have allowed hatred and lawlessness to enter their CPU for the purpose of possessing them. Once they are possessed, he can easily spread his virus throughout their hard drive systems and devour them. He knows how much they mean to the CIA, how much it hurts them, and that's why he loves doing it. He learned at the time of the Transgression that what hurt CEO and His BT the most was any injury or loss of Their beloved Heirs. And since he didn't give a hoot about them, it didn't bother him a bit. But it certainly bothers the CIA. After all, Traitor and his gang heard Them weep profusely after the Mutation.

He summons his unsavory cohorts to a meeting. When they have gathered before him and he begins to speak, he is nearly foaming at the mouth as he spews out orders. "We must destroy this Ransom! You must research any and every possible angle on how we can take Him down! He is ensnared in matter, so this task shouldn't be that hard. Do I make myself clear?" he hisses, fully expecting positive nods in response to his command. "And if you can't get *this* job done right, I'm going to take some of *you* down!" he threatens. Looking at each other, they nod sheepishly and go fearfully to work.

Ransom walks and preaches from town to town and city to city. He delivers the good news of the AVP. He tells all who will listen that He has been sent by UF to bring the AVP to whosoever will accept it. It will immunize them in two ways. One, it will restore and clean up their hard drives back to pre-Mutation days. They will once again have access to spiritual wholeness. And two, the AVP provides a wireless link that reconnects their CPU to the Ultimate Host—Central. When their physical bodies, the outer-shell hardware or housing, finally wears out, this link/connection will allow the CIA to provide them with new housing. All who freely choose to be connected will automatically receive free upgrades and have their unique DNA serial codes registered and saved in a file entitled "Ransom's Restored" on a tiny disc secured in the third vault at CIA Headquarters. He continues, "*I am the CGS (the Cosmic Guidance System). No one can get to Central without Me. I am the way!*"

Moving within Central's power, Ransom touches the sick, and they are healed. Word spreads from town to town, and more orblings follow. Those who are possessed are restored when touched by Him. He preaches the Voice wherever He goes. Throngs of orblings follow Him to learn of the good news.

No orbling has ever spoken with such authority. Everyone is astounded by His wisdom. On a grassy knoll, He shares more of the mysteries of the CIA, expounding:

Every good tree bears good fruit,
But a bad tree bears bad fruit.
A good tree cannot bear bad fruit,
Nor can a bad tree bear good fruit.
Every tree that does not bear good fruit
Will be cut down.
Therefore, by their fruits you will know them.
Not everyone who says to Me, "Restorer, Restorer,"
Shall enter Headquarters, but only they who do the
Will of the Universal Father.

Ransom has been successfully teaching, healing, and sharing the Voice for approximately three years, and Traitor is absolutely beside himself. He is going nuts because he hasn't been able to stop the Son of CEO from spreading the AVP. The beautiful, magnificent, regal Rotiart of long ago has turned into a maniacal, foaming at-the-mouth, crazy, mean, jumbled mess of raw nerves. Ransom has successfully delivered the AVP to Favored. Large throngs of orblings have been exposed to the truth of Central, and more and more orblings are being born again as they accept the gift of the AVP and have their names added to the file on the disc called Ransom's Restored. All of Traitor's attempts and attacks to destroy the Son of CEO have not yet succeeded. Ransom continues teaching orblings how to treat one another with love and understanding, and to beware of Traitor and his deceptions.

THE THIRD COOKIE

One evening while Ransom is in the town garden, petitioning for the continued restoration of the hard drives of His Heirs, the BT hovers over Him. This encounter lasts much longer than all the others. It is extremely intense. The BT infuses Him with more power and love. Then He is handed the third and final chocolate chip cookie. CEO and the BT inform Him that this is the last one, and soon He will once again set foot on Central soil, because His work is almost completed. The only thing left for Him to do is to activate the AVP. His heart leaps at the thought of returning home again now that His reason for coming is almost fulfilled. He feels strangely homesick. He happily receives the cookie, and after several minutes, the chips in the cookie have downloaded and revealed to Him *how* the AVP must be activated. Unlike the other cookies, this one is far from sweet and leaves a horribly bitter aftertaste on His tongue. He tries to wash it away with a cup of water, but the bitterness remains. Shortly afterwards, His stomach begins to burn and fill with an indescribable pain, and He doubles over. Lying on the ground in agony He cries out to the BT, *"Please let this bitter cookie pass from Me! But if it must be so, help Me get through it."* Although He is in far too much pain and turmoil to even notice Them, CEO and the BT lovingly hover over Him until morning.

At sunrise, many of Traitor's converts and all those with hardened

181

CPU's think they have found a way to silence Ransom. Even one of His closest compatriots sells Him out for 30 coins by telling the mob where they may find Him. Just like those who gathered to follow Ransom, many have gathered together to come against Him. This day, the local government is going to put two convicted orblings to death who have been found guilty of crimes. They are to be sentenced by being nailed to a tree. They beat them before they finally nail them up and leave them, hanging, to die. Behind the scenes, the Castaways work many into a frenzied mob. Most of them are so deceived that they don't even know what they are doing. Filled with hatred and hopelessness, they enjoy hurting others. They have long since been deceived into believing there will be no day of reckoning, no justice, and no accountability.

ACTIVATION BEGINS

The angry mob grabs Ransom. Just as the Voice teaches righteousness, Traitor whispers and teaches treachery. They kick Him, and they beat Him. They drag Him before a mock court, with no intention of delivering any justice. They want to kill Him because everybody thinks He is the Son of CEO. He moves with authority and power, and His teachings are changing the way orblings think and act, which is threatening to those who are warped and twisted. They yell obscenities at Him and ask Him, "If You really are the Son of CEO, why don't You call for help? Why doesn't the CIA come rushing to Your aid, if You claim to be the Son of CEO?"

Those who have come to love and follow Him are still at home in bed, just waking up. The few who are with Him are outnumbered and overpowered. Fear grips their hearts as Traitor's unseen presence permeates the area and fills all those who shun the Voice with hatred and power. It seems as though insanity has gripped the masses. They beat Ransom mercilessly, and His transmission fluid is flying everywhere. At last, with the help of Traitor, someone gets the brilliant idea of finishing Him off and nailing him on a tree between two convicted felons. After all, He has always preached about trees and how they needed to bear good fruit.

Watching the scene, the Atom Smasher Specialist is now rubbing his hands together, salivating in anticipation over his imminent victory. He relishes the charmingly macabre idea of Ransom hanging and dying on a tree between two convicted felons. He knows that to the CIA, trees symbolize life. Knowing many secrets of the Tree of Life, he cackles to himself and thinks how deliciously unjust it will be, that the Son of CEO, nailed on the middle tree, will die and become the Head of this unsavory trio. He is also well aware of the significance of the number three to the CIA.

The mob grabs Ransom and elevates Him up against the middle tree. They stretch out His arms, and they nail His wrists to the tree. Then they cross His feet and nail through them gleefully, and with more taunting and mocking, they yell out, "Let's see if this tree will now bear better fruit, with the Son of CEO hanging on it!" In all their ignorance, they do not see that they have created the perfect fractal effigy. His hanging body outstretched in the shape of a cross is symbolically watering a tree with His transmission fluid. They laugh and jeer and spit on Him. The very things He made for their life and enjoyment are being used against Him to try to destroy Him. They put a sign over His head that reads: "CEO of the Prevailies." They party and dance around Him for hours, having no compassion for His suffering and pain. His transmission fluid keeps flowing out until there is none left, and He breathes His last few breaths. Before He physically expires at three in the afternoon, that day, He looks up one last time and says, *"Forgive them, for they are clueless."* Then with His very last breath, He says, *"TLC Mission accomplished!"*

A.S.S. and His Castaways are celebrating like never before. They are even feeling confident enough to discuss how they will overtake Central in the near future. They have destroyed Ransom and killed Him on the very thing that the CIA has symbolically used for creating life.

This, they believe, is truly their finest hour, the pinnacle of all they have hoped for. Favored will forever belong to them, they think, and now they can easily finish off the remaining Heirs. "Ah, the sweet smell of victory," declares Traitor as his underlings lift him up over their shoulders, raucously cheer, and joyfully dance about.

THE NUCLEAR VEIL IS RENT

Suddenly Favored starts to shake violently, Fun stops shining, the sky grows black, and with a horrifically loud clap of thunder, a bright lightening strike flashes across the blackness. The sound of a violent tear can be heard from every point on the orb. The veil of separation between the physical and spiritual dimensions, which formed from the nuclear blast at the time the Atom was split, is now completely rent.

Bittersweet, having heard what they did to her son, rushes to the tree and cries. The sweetness and privilege of carrying the Son of CEO has now turned excruciatingly bitter. She fully comprehends the meaning of the name she was given at birth. This pain is more than she thinks she can bear. He had moved in such great power and taught with such amazing authority, this did not make sense. How could He have been killed and defeated this way?

After watching the brutality Ransom faced before He died, the compatriot who sold Him out could not stand to live with what he had done, so he took his own life and hanged himself on a tree outside of town and died.

Bittersweet's remaining family and close friends take Ransom's mutilated, lifeless body off the tree and lay Him in a burial cloth. A rich man who loved Him and followed His ways gives Him a special burial cave. After wrapping Him carefully, they put Him inside and, with the help of many orblings, push an extremely heavy stone in front of the cave to seal it. Completely saddened, exhausted, and emotionally defeated, they all head home, not knowing how they can possibly go on.

THE "THREE OF LIFE"

After three days, there is another huge orbquake. The stone rolls away and Ransom walks out of His tomb. The Son of CEO is raised from the dead by the CIA. He visits His foster family, close friends, and some of His followers to let them know He has overcome death. He shares meals with them and tells them that He is preparing a place for them and that where He is going they may also be. News spreads far and wide of His sightings. "He's alive! He's alive!" the orblings shout. "Our Restorer lives!" is the cry of the land. He tells His Restored Ones that when their time comes, He will be their Cosmic Guidance System, for He knows the way to Central and will escort them home. He also leaves them with a comforting message. *"In addition to the Voice helping you overcome the orb and Traitor so that you might live well, I will send you the Beloved Teacher (BT), who will guide you, hold you, and comfort you in My absence, until we are once again reunited. I came to the orb so that you might have life and have it more abundantly."*

As He waves goodbye, Ransom is caught up in the air by CIA's molecular transporter, and in the blinking of an eye He is gone. Once again at CEO's side, the birthed aspect and beloved Son, with visible scars from being the AVP Restorer, is reunited with the CIA and is completely whole again. Tears of joy flow sweetly from everyone at CIA. In the Great Ruby Hall, all the loyal Secret Agents gather to welcome

Ransom back and praise Him.

They joyfully celebrate His wondrous TLC accomplishments through His Forgiveness Based Immunization initiative. Thought activated, the giant screen springs to life again. Everyone can hardly wait to once more savor the brilliance and precious miracle that took place on Favored. They petition CEO to push the replay button so they may all witness the miracle once again. Appearing across the huge screen, the heart-gripping drama and greatest story ever told begins to play back. There are no dry eyes to be found in the Great Hall. When the heart-warming ending is once again revealed, sober smiles return to the viewer's faces. Applause from the millions attending rings out, followed by a standing ovation. The Great Ruby Hall is now beating to the rhythm of new pulsars, as if born-again, from the victorious conclusion.

A picture of the Universe appears. Then a bold crimson cross is seen superimposed over it. At the intersection of the cross hangs Favored. It is the living, breathing, pulsating heart of the Universe. The Mutation had created a blockage to CIA's life force. CEO's aspect was incarnated to perform a subatomic (nano) bypass surgery and transfusion. Ransom has traveled through the intersection/crossroad of time and lovingly fixed the crux of the matter when He watered the middle tree He was nailed upon and activated the AVP with His life-giving transmission fluid. He has donated His perfect transmission fluid to the heart of the matter—The Tree of Life Cross (TLC). And He has graciously restored the broken connection, freeing all virally-infected Heirs who accept His sacrifice. CEO has always said that *the mysteries of the Universe and its secrets are to be found in its extreme sizes."* Having received the ultimate transfusion, the Tree of Life has been reconnected and its spine reinforced by CEO's TLC. All that is needed now is more healing time. Ransom's Restored will soon give the Tri-Unity a healthy

Body and will dwell with the CIA in wholeliness at Headquarters. The Agents are completely flabbergasted once they grasp the significance and brilliance of His sacrifice.

Observing their reactions, the CIA is moved to share one of Its greatest mysteries. CEO points to the screen where the crimson cross is and says:

The secret to the Tree of Life may be found in the Three of Life! The Collective I Am is a Tri-Unity made up of the Matter, Time, and Space continuum. Matter simply always is! That is why I am also called The Great I Am.

When is a tree a tree? Is it a tree when it is in the form of a seed under the ground, is it a tree when it is a sapling, is it a tree when it is full grown, or is it a tree when it finally returns to the ground? The answer is that it is always a tree! But because of the Time and Space continuum, the differing perspectives of its various stages of expression or growth are revealed to a viewer, dependent upon where and when the viewer is able to observe it. Time and Space are the dimensional aspects or arms of the Tri-Unity that change and move, creating the unending circle of life with its kaleidoscopic effects.

Observe also that every atom is basically composed of three things: protons, neutrons, and electrons—a miniature circle of life with a nucleus. It is a full-spectrum cross.

Have you not noticed that the cross has a dynamic mathematical base? It is a precise geometric fractal representation of the Collective I Am! I created everything through the cross. It is the glue that holds My creations together. Stemming from My gravitas, this fractal literally holds the Universe in agreement. It can be seen in everything I have created, from the massive down to the microscopic. Your bodies, and those of the Heirs, are filled with my fractal design. You are both fearfully and wonderfully made. My fingerprints can even be found in the microscopic membranes of the tissues of the Heirs. They are a family of structural scaffolding proteins in the shape of the cross that scientists have named laminin, and they function to literally hold one cell to the next.

To reiterate, I make everything through the cross. It is the glue that keeps everything in unison. I made the orb through the cross and I saved it through the cross! Now ponder this when you see it or look at it: The vertical line or trunk is the main head. The horizontal line creates the arms. There is a left and right arm. The trunk beneath the arms is the body. Every cross has an intersection. The intersection is the heart or nucleus in every cross. The heart of the Universe (Favored) is given an axis that tilts toward its spatial energy Fun, the other stars, and the CIA. The heart of the Heirs is also given an axis that tilts toward its spatial energy—I their Maker.

When you count the lines that make up a cross, you find three above and one below. The three above represent the spirit world or head, made up of the matter, time, and space continuum. The one below represents the physical world or body, completing the Tri-Unity. The Head represents matter, the Right arm represents time, and the Left arm represents space.

The Head is matter and everything that matters stems from it. Matter and CEO's gravitas will and bend or change the Time and Space continuum arms. The Right arm is a time continuum and carries out the will of the Head. The Left arm is a space continuum (birthing womb) from which all matter flows and in which all matter lies. Note that the Right and Left arms (time & space) can move up to the Head, down to the lower body, or sideways, just like your own arms. The Head (matter) remains. It wills the Arms and the Body to move.

Three is the number of the CIA. Three is the number of the points on the head of a cross. When you add up all the points on a cross, they total four. Four is the number of My creation, i.e., the physical aspect. The Universe represents the physical realm that houses the body of the CIA, its Heirs.

Ponder the four corners of the orb—north, south, east, and west. How about the dimensions of height, length, width, and breadth, as well as up, down, left, and right? Then consider the four seasons—winter, summer, spring, and fall, each of which contains three sets of four months. If you add the number three, which represents the Tri-Unity or Head of the cross, to the number four, which represents the body or the physical world, you get the number of completion—seven.

Then notice My Ten Instructions given to the Heirs in the User's Manual. It is no coincidence that the first three deal with the Tri-Unity. The next seven deal completely with the body. The CIA's mathematical expressions may be found in all Its creations, and most definitely in Its symbolic cross. My signature, the cross, may be discovered in every aspect of My Creation, from the extremely massive down to the microscopic, by all who wish to find it.

Then CEO concludes His teaching with, *"Let them that have ears to hear understand the mystery of the cross!"*

A.D. (ANTIDOTE DELIVERED)

First hundreds, then thousands, and then tens of thousands accept the free gift of the AVP. As soon as they accept it, they are healed and begin thinking anew. They are now able to live more victoriously and understand their true heritage. Knowing that they are the Heirs, they now begin to act like Heirs. With the added help of the Beloved Teacher they live by the standards that the Voice gives them and look forward to when they will complete the upper body and inherit Nucle-Eye Headquarters.

The CIA now waits for the sifting process to finish. It will only take a few more thousand orb years, which for the CIA is just the blink of an eye. Inspired by the BT, more and more orblings begin to document all that they hear and learn from the Voice. Over a long period of time, the completed scrolls come together to form a book called *The Written Voice.* This manuscript gives His children another way to learn. Throughout the years, millions had become tone deaf to the Voice, although many continue to hear a "small, still voice" that helps them decipher right from wrong. He hopes that when they read *The Written Voice,* the small, still voice remaining will find confirmation.

Thousands of believers now preach the good news of Ransom the Restorer. They tell everyone who will listen that the only way to be reconnected to the Ultimate Host is to accept the free gift of the AVP.

The reconnection fees had been impossible for any orbling to pay. Their DNA credit cards had expired when they transgressed CEO's boundary. That is why the CIA lovingly sent Their Only Begotten Aspect. By shedding His perfect DNA He established an acceptable credit card and payment method. Ransom paid the reconnection tab in full. All that is required now from orblings is that they gratefully accept His sacrificial payment. Whosoever accepts Ransom's free gift is allowed to use His password. The only password that allows entry into, and prepays access to, the Ultimate PaidPal System is the name of Ransom.

Millions come to appreciate the sacrificial gift that will save them, bring them reconnection rights, ultimately heal them, and get their names added to the file at Headquarter called Ransom's Restored.

In the meanwhile, the CIA is allowing the growth process to continue until all the names filed on the disc in Vault One have played out. When that disc finishes playing, the season of growth is ended and the great endowment harvest begins. At that time, all the names who have accepted the AVP will be completely restored, given new bodies with incorruptible battery packs, and receive permanent wireless connection. All names will be scrutinized and checked against Ransom's Restored list. Those who refused His gift and think they are good enough, or by their actions amass enough credits to pay their own way, will be surprised. Because throughout the history of orblings, the Voice has beckoned and pleaded that they come back to Him and under His protection—like a mother hen who lovingly gathers her chicks under her wings. Those who run off and think warmth and love may be found elsewhere will suffer the consequences. Love can only manifest if it is accepted. It is never love if it is forced.

THE A.S.S. IS HAD

Many orblings who have become possessed by Traitor and his gang act wickedly and persecute the Voice heeders who, after the death of Ransom, are now called the Restored. There is a surge in learning, and hearts are changed from the unleashing of the AVP into the orb, as well as the BT. Whenever an orbling receives the AVP, the Beloved Teacher has permission to come into their lives and minister to them. The Voice shunners cannot understand this power from above and try to destroy those who walk in new wholeness. However, the numbers of those saved and restored grow every orb day, and all the combined, deceptive forces of Traitor are unable to stop the forward march of salvation.

Traitor, who had just assumed that the Heirs would be completely defeated when Ransom was killed, is slowly waking up to a strange new reality. More and more Heirs are being restored, and fewer and fewer are being deceived. He and his cohorts are not able to exact the same influence over them, much to their chagrin. Many of those restored now actually begin to see through his destructive schemes. He had thought by instigating Ransom's murder, the CIA would collapse and the Heirs would forever lose their Cosmic Guidance System. After that, he figured invasion of Nucle-Eye would be a piece of cake. But he has discovered that when Ransom shed His perfect transmission fluid, an antidote was released into the orb. And it didn't occur to him, or he just forgot, that CEO could simply raise His Son's DNA.

The realization that he has, once again, been outsmarted by CEO, slowly seeps in. The sweet smell of victory he was already sniffing has turned into a fleeting vapor on steroids. Like a volcano just before it blows its top, the heat wave crawls from his lower extremities up to his neck. His face turns red, he is flushed, and steam comes out of both his ears. In a frenzied tirade, spinning around like a top, he becomes slightly airborne, lifting off the ground, while the vessels in his neck look like they are going to pop. His underlings stare at him and are amused, but they dare not show it, for fear of retaliation. Once such a regal and refined being, he has morphed into a maniacal fiend who is clearly losing it. In spite of the fact that his demeanor has changed and taken many turns since his exile from Headquarters, some of his behavioral outbursts still manage to take his buddies by surprise. A.S.S. comes to the brutal realization that his days are numbered. All he has left now is his last hurrah.

EPILOGUE

For CEO so loved the orb that He gave His only begotten Aspect so that whosoever accepts the gift of the AVP shall be restored to life everlasting.

By speaking and believing the transgressor's petition, you too may be saved:

"Father, I confess that I'm a sinner, and realize that I am incapable of paying the price for my salvation. Thank you for the sacrifice of Your beloved Son Jesus dying on the cross and shedding His precious blood, making the full and final payment on my behalf, so that I might be saved and reconciled to You. Save me and come into my life, and help me."

ABOUT THE AUTHOR

Marion Wadleigh, the daughter of both mother and father scientists, was born in a Catholic monastery in West Germany shortly after her parents, fearing for their lives, had fled East Germany. The Russian government had planned to ship them to Moscow, where they would have been employed against their will. Having already lived under the oppression of Nazism, they chose death if caught for the possibility of having freedom and liberty, and they fled when they found a momentary window of opportunity. They left with nothing but the clothes on their backs, two small children, and one on the way. After Marion was delivered by a nun three months later, the family lived in a refugee camp for the first two years of her life until her parents moved to Switzerland and started a laboratory. Six years later, they were asked to come to the United States when their expertise was needed on a sensitive assignment.

As a teenager, Marion lost her beloved brother, a Marine, to the Vietnam War. The pain she experienced from her grief caused her to begin crying out to God searching for the meaning of life. Although she always believed in God, she didn't believe that Jesus Christ was the Son of God. In her mind, He was a good man, and she thought that if you stand up for what is right you generally pay a price. Having a scientific background, she could not believe in something without facts. She thought most of the stories in the Bible were just that—cute and interesting stories, especially the one about Adam and Eve.

As a young adult she worked for a leading aerospace company where she became friends with a woman who invited her to attend a home bible study group. Many of her associates and friends also shared their differing faiths and viewpoints. As God continued to provoke her curiosity, she began reading the Bible in earnest. However, her intentions were to ultimately disprove Christ. As she studied the gospels, much to her chagrin, she found the opposite to be true. When she came to that realization, she wept. She had searched for light and truth even in dark places, but God in His love led her to His ultimate truth—the truth that brings grace and salvation through the gift of His Son.

To order additional copies of Nucle-Eye, fill out this form and return.

First Name	Last Name

Street Address	Apt/ Unit	City	State	Zip Code

No. of Copies	Price Ea. $12.95	Add $4.50 S&H Per Book	Total

Send form and check or money order to:

**CrossTree Publishing
P.O. Box 392
Bayfield, CO 81122-0392**

You may also contact us by fax: (970) 884-8007

CROSSTREE PUBLISHING